EDITORIAL Jo

In peacetime expenditure on defence is, almost without exception, looked upon as a necessary evil. It is always expensive and, except in war, shows little return for the vast sums of money that it absorbs. Under such circumstances any democratic government must be expected to seek ways of reducing the cost of armaments both to increase the finance available for other areas and to satisfy their own and the public's desire to see reductions in taxation. This is a situation of mutual advantage in which the public sees its money, or less of it, well spent, and the government can divert money into projects of social value which both advance its own policies and improve its chances of re-election. There is of course a limit to this in that fears among the public that the defences of the country are weak would have a serious effect on public morale and the status of the government and, on more than one occasion, such fears have generated a substantial increase in defence spending.

In times of recession, such as that that existed in the 1920s and 1930s or that which exists now, the defence departments are continually under pressure to minimise costs and anybody who can produce a reasonably convincing idea to save money will be listened to with sympathy, and often encouragement, by the government. Thus between the wars, the Admiralty were pressurised by circumstances into accepting smaller ships, less sophisticated ships in some cases, and less of them, knowing that they were not completely satisfactory. The inefficiency of the AA systems in British warships at the outbreak of the Second World War was as much, if not more, to do with the fact that the money to develop and produce an efficient fire control system and the weapons to go with it was not available. The Admiralty knew of this situation before the war and any criticism has to be developed in terms of whether or not they had their priorities right in spending money on other projects rather than a simple assumption that they should have known better.

At various times in the 1920s and early 1930s proposals were made both, officially (usually in the hope of international agreement) and unofficially for smaller and hence cheaper battleships, and for the abandonment of battleships, altogether as obsolete. Both these ideas were listened to and encouraged by the governments of the time.

At the present time there is, in Britain, a controversial public debate in progress on what type of ship the Admiralty should build in the future. The argument revolves around whether the Royal Navy should continue with its traditional designs or switch to a short, broad beamed, type claimed to be equally, if not more, efficient and cheaper. On one side is the Admiralty and its design team at Bath which has produced the Type 23 frigate – a traditional vessel in form and cost restricted but nevertheless modern and sophisticated. On the other is a small private company which has used the media and the government to promote its S90, a short, broad beamed design claimed to be cheaper, of high stability and capable of carrying more weapons and equipment than a traditional type of equal or greater displacement. Unfortunately the debate is in the hands of a largely inexpert media who repeat claims without understanding them to a public which is ignorant of the complexities of warship design and can only see the efforts of private enterprise being resisted by civil service bureaucracy.

I have yet to see a reasonable or even partial set of particulars of the S90 so it is difficult to make any sound judgement on the claims made for the design. It is obvious that a broad beamed ship does have a higher level of stability than a narrow beam one and that it can therefore carry more topweight and/or higher topweights, hence the claim to be able to carry more weapons and higher (and hence greater range) radar aerials. However, many questions come to mind and I am still waiting to hear them mentioned in the public debate on the subject. The vessel is claimed as cheaper, and a smaller hull and diesel propulsion would save money but the most expensive items in warships are their weapons and sensors and if more of these are carried the cost goes up again, possibly by more than the saving. At one time claims were made that S90 could reach the same speed as the Type 23 with the same engine power and fuel consumption which, to say the least, is highly dubious. I would guess that a short, broad beamed ship would have a poor motion in any sort of seaway which raises questions of crew and equipment efficiency in rough weather – bearing in mind the Royal Navy's principal areas of operation – the North Sea, Arctic, North Atlantic and now the South Atlantic, this is a very important point. Broad beamed ships, although possessing high stability, heel much more when damaged on one side. What, given that masts are usually placed well apart to reduce mutual interference between radar aerials, will be the radar outfit of S90 which at present has only one tall mast? I mention all this not so much as criticism of the design as to point out that such things are seldom, if at all, mentioned – the debate is much more on the level of 'it's got more guns and it's cheap so it must be better' – I would be much happier, and in a better position to criticise or agree, if more facts and figures were attached to the claims for the S90.

SOME THORNYCROFT DESIGNS

By DJ Lyon

One of the most fascinating aspects of the enormous Thornycroft Collection of plans and associated documents now held in the National Maritime Museum is the vast number of designs for vessels which were never built that it includes. Unfortunately most other shipbuilders' collections of plans only include vessels which were actually built (the smaller and less important, though still interesting, Pollock's Collection is the only other major exception). The interest of the often weird and wonderful designs produced by Thornycroft is added to by the fact that much of the correspondence about them is still surviving. It is hoped to include full details of all surviving designs in the forthcoming 'Thornycroft List' to be published by the Museum, but meanwhile illustrations of some of the most unusual of these projects may interest and amuse other warship enthusiasts as much as they do the writer.

Of course many of the designs are very similar to those used in the building of vessels at Thornycroft's Chiswick, Woolston and Hampton yards, or by subcontractors at other locations. Many represent part of the process of developing the designs of those vessels. There are, however, a few which are totally unlike anything built by Thornycroft's, or indeed anyone else.

Our first example, the 'Design for shallow draft gunboat for the Imperial Russian Government' (Chiswick plan 2089 dated 27 February 1884) is most definitely a case in point. By the 1880s, Thornycroft's, besides being successful builders of steam launches and torpedo boats, had also developed a promising line of river steamers utilising light steel construction, tunnel sterns, and the Thornycroft invention of the 'guide blade screw' or 'turbine propeller', a ducted propeller, to obtain the shallowest possible draft. At this stage they were very much against the cruder and cheaper expedient of using stern paddle wheels to get the same result

Shallow draft gunboat for Russia (Chiswick plan 2089, 27 February 1884).
NMM

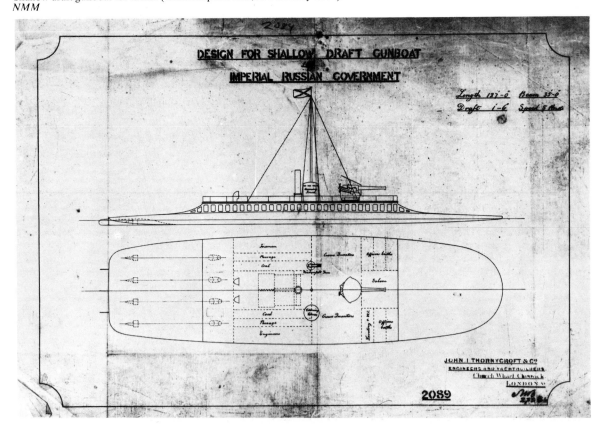

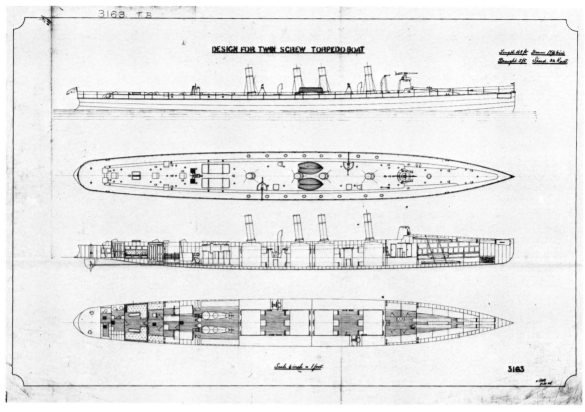

Twin screw torpedo boat (Chiswick plan 3163, December 1886).
NMM

(though they built steamers of this type later). Therefore, when they were asked to submit a design to Russian requirements they utilised four of these propellers, powered by the same type of compound engines used in contemporary second class torpedo boats. The shield for the big 6in gun, and probably the conning tower as well, were of 1½in thick steel. The conning tower was off-centre, as was the 5-barrel 0.45in Nordenfelt machine gun. There is no mention of where this slipper-shaped monster was meant to operate, but the fact that the engines had direct injection instead of surface condensers, and therefore presumably could take advantage of a constant supply of fresh water, probably means she was intended for river use, perhaps in Siberia. She would have cost £20,000 exclusive of armament.

Unfortunately there is no correspondence with the next design, a twin screw torpedo boat (Chiswick plan 3163), but this comes from a time (December 1886) when Thornycroft's were already thinking in terms of bigger and better torpedo boats, a line of development which was soon to result in the torpedo boat destroyer. This vessel, with its four water tube boilers, twin bow torpedo tubes and three quick-firing guns can be seen as a predecessor of the *Daring* and *Decoy*, Thornycroft's first destroyers.

On 25 May 1893 the torpedo cruiser design shown in Chiswick plan 6151 was offered to Captain T Damering

of the Royal Norwegian Navy. This was really a cross between a torpedo gunboat and a destroyer. The elevated platforms forward for two 6pdr guns covered the 'heads'. The bigger guns just abaft the funnels were 12 pdrs, whilst the poop mounted two 3pdrs. The 4-barrel machine guns on the bridge were of 1in calibre, whilst the single torpedo tubes offset to port and starboard respectively at the breaks of poop and forecastle were probably for 18in torpedoes. The plan shows how the boilers and machinery were protected by coal bunkers. Six water tube boilers at a pressure of 200lb were to provide steam to the two triple expansion engines, giving a speed of 22 knots with 4400ihp. The crew were to be provided with 24 rifles, 24 cutlasses and 12 revolvers. The price, exclusive of torpedoes and ammunition, was £55,000.

Just before the First World War Thornycroft's produced a whole series of minelayer designs for Turkey, none of which were built, though some river gunboats were supplied. Woolston drawing number 6253 of 1911 shows one of the heaviest-armed designs, a cruiser-type vessel (others were on destroyer lines). The 120 mines stowed on the lower deck aft would be brought up onto the main deck and laid through a single stern port; one would have thought a cumbersome and slow process. The bow and stern guns were 100mm (4in), with two 12pdrs on either side. An alternative version of this design shows two 45cm (18in)

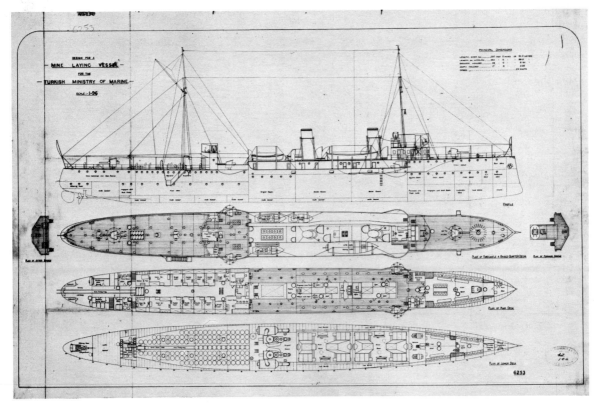

Cruiser minelayer for Turkey (Woolston drawing No 6253, 1 May 1911).
NMM

torpedo tubes on the upper deck. The triple expansion engines were intended to give her a speed of 24 knots. The price was 'say £85,000'.

At much the same time Thornycroft's were producing a series of designs for 'motor torpedo boats', in fact merely versions of steam torpedo boats powered by a couple of diesel engines. A whole series of these were designed for Italy (Thornycroft's had provided many designs of destroyers and torpedo craft for building by Pattinson's of Naples for the Italian Navy), but the design shown in Woolston drawing 6392 was intended for Greece. Two 45cm torpedo tubes are supplemented by a 76mm (3in) gun. The top speed of 26 knots would have made this quite a useful vessel for a small navy.

The 'motor paddle canoe' in the undated plan, Woolston number O/A 235 is probably from late 1914 or early 1915, and may have been intended as a miniature river gunboat for Mesopotamia. Unfortunately, little else is known about it, though the quick-firing gun forward is probably a 3pdr.

The concrete harbour blocking vessel in Head Office plan 16752 is similarly devoid of detailed explanation, but it seems very likely that this 1917 design, with its submarine-shaped hull fitted for rapid flooding was designed for the purpose for which old cruisers were eventually used, the blocking of the German submarine bases at Zeebrugge and Ostend.

In 1930 Thornycroft's were approached by the Dutch to design a very large and powerful flotilla leader, with a specification which eventually developed into the Dutch designed and built *Tromp* class of light cruisers. The flush-decked single funnel design number T548 was produced in 1931, and was one of a series, the others all looking more like the then conventional two-funnelled, forecastle-decked destroyer. There was 1in protective plating on the deck and 1½ on the sides covered the magazine and machinery spaces. Eight 120mm (4.7in) guns, 4–40mm (2pdr) pompoms and two triple 21in torpedo tubes made up the armament.

A seaplane completed the offensive equipment of this powerful small warship. The Dutch were asking for a maximum speed of at least 33 knots. Thornycroft's Dutch agent wrote: 'My impression is that the French Yards will be the most severe competitors in this particular case and therefore we will have to handle the matter of price somewhat diplomatically.' In fact Thornycroft's would have charged £14,000 if the Dutch had decided to use this design for a ship built in Holland.

In the late 1920s, Thornycroft's working in co-operation with Supermarine's, developed a design for a small aircraft carrier to operate flying boat fighters, which were to fly off a flight deck forward using trolleys, and be recovered by taxi-ing up the inclined plane of the stern which extended underwater. By 1932 this design had developed into the form shown in plan T739. This quite elegant small ship was to operate a force of some seven floatplanes by catapulting them off the forecastle, and recovering them either by crane or by a Hein mat which could be towed behind, onto which the aircraft would taxi, and then be winched on board. In practical trials the mat more often resulted in bent aircraft than effective recoveries. The armament of the ship was three 4.7in guns and four AA pompoms. Destroyer-type machinery would give 28 knots. Thornycroft's prepared quite elaborate brochures on this design, but without any success in selling the idea. An equal lack of success was experienced by a wartime design for a light aircraft carrier to carry fighters on deck, which made the Director of Naval Construction so annoyed about what he considered to be a waste of draughtsman's time that he threatened to take over Thornycroft's design staff for the Admiralty.

One of the more original designs to come out of the Second World War was a small destroyer designed for coastal use as virtually an updating of the First World War 'S' class. Design T1341 shows the basic version of this design primarily intended for anti-E-boat work. The hull lines were specially designed for speed in shallow water (12 to 15 fathoms), and a very large rudder was fitted for quick steering. This type was intended to fill the gap between the steam gunboat and the destroyer proper. The version shown, armed with 2 old 4in guns, a 2pdr bow chaser in a turret, 6 Oerlikons and 4 fixed MTB type 21in torpedo tubes was intended principally for night work. The other anti-E-boat version

was also intended for day work and had a single twin high angle 4in mounting and eight Oerlikons instead of the previous gun armament, though retaining the torpedo tubes. An anti-submarine patrol version was similar to the first version except in adding Asdic and depth charges, whilst a general purpose version was intended to share the same armament as the second version except for having only a single 4in in the high angle mount, and adding a high speed mine-sweep aft. The designed speed in favourable conditions was intended to be 37½ knots.

Amongst Thornycroft's most successful designs during the First World War and for many years later were the coastal motor boats, with stepped hulls and launching a torpedo from a stern trough. Early in the second conflict the growing E-boat menace caused the suggestion to be made of using these well-tried hulls as motor gunboats with an armament of fixed 20mm guns intended to be used like those of a fighter plane by aiming the whole boat. Head Office plan number 23370 shows one of two such surviving designs. The cannon would be supplemented by quadruple Vickers 'K' machine guns mounted on the Scarff ring behind the steering shelter.

The Type 4 'Hunts' *Brecon* and *Brissenden* were very different from the other ships of the 'Hunt' class, and a lot of thought had gone into their design. It is not surprising that Thornycroft's designed improved, enlarged

'Motor paddle canoe' (Woolston drawing no O/A 235, 1914 or 1915). *NMM*

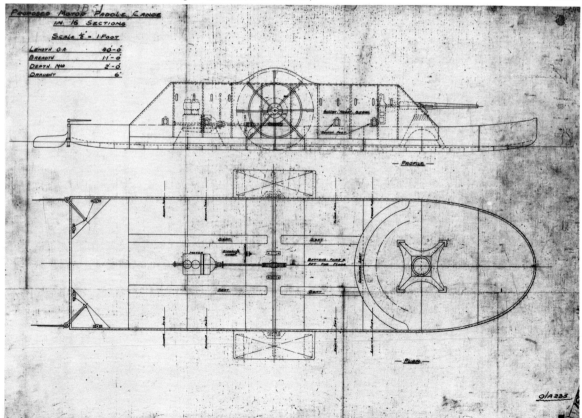

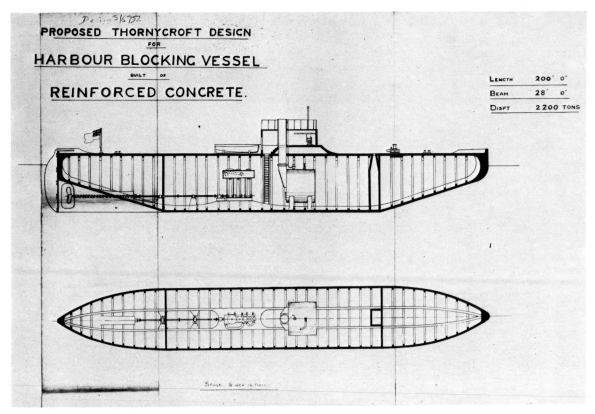

Concrete harbour blocking vessel (Head Office plan 16752, 1917).
NMM

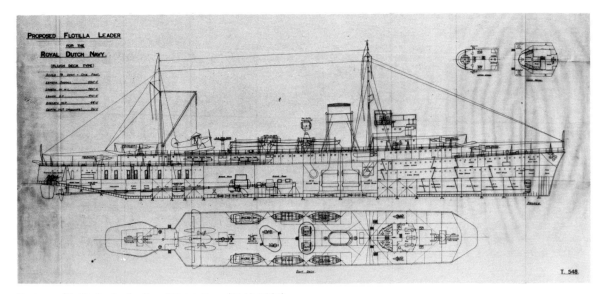

Destroyer Flotilla leader for Royal Dutch Navy (T548, 1931).
NMM

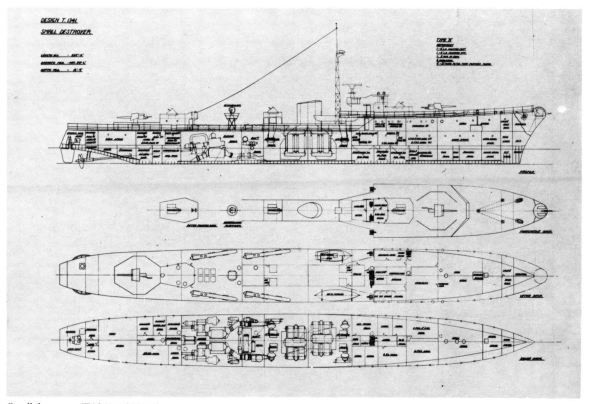

Small destroyer (T1341, 1939-45).
NMM

versions whilst the war was still on, and continued to adapt the design to various sizes and armaments after the war was over. Design TWY 1737 as the initials suggest was a joint tender by Thornycroft's, White's and Yarrow's to the Brazilian Navy in the early 1950s, but its looks betray the fact that it was actually designed by Thornycroft's. The hull is that of an enlarged *Brecon*, the armament that of a *Daring* class destroyer, but with more emphasis on 40mm AA guns, and less on torpedo tubes. The Thornycroft-type funnel is characteristic of a whole series of designs of this period, although in this particular case there was an alternative twin funnel design. Maximum speed was 35 knots. It is perhaps not too fanciful to see in this design the ancestor of today's *Niteroi* class built by Vosper-Thornycroft for Brazil.

NOTE

For further details of Thornycroft history see *A Hundred Years of Specialised Shipbuilding and Engineering* by K C Barnaby (Hutchinson, 1964) and articles by D J Lyon in *Model Shipwright* Nos 17, 18 and 20.

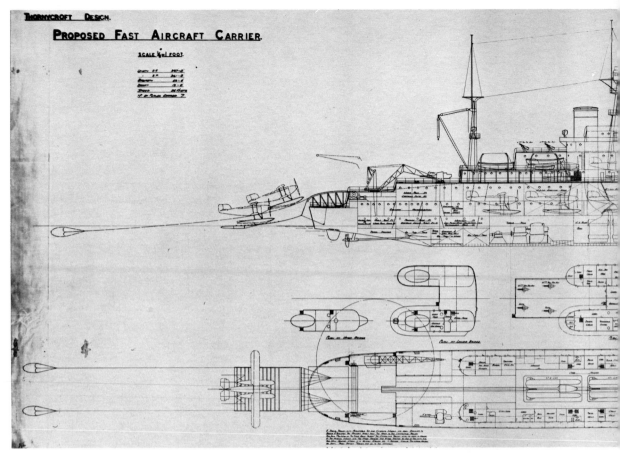

THORNYCROFT DESIGN.

PROPOSED FAST AIRCRAFT CARRIER.

SCALE ⅛"=1 FOOT.

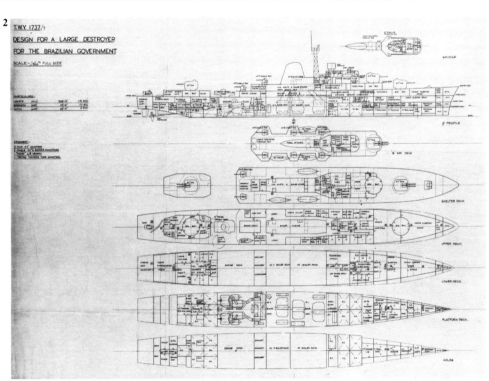

2 T.WY 1737/3

DESIGN FOR A LARGE DESTROYER
FOR THE BRAZILIAN GOVERNMENT

SCALE = 1/64" FULL SIZE

1 Proposed fast aircraft carrier
(T739, 1932).
NMM

2 Large destroyer for Brazil (TWY 1737,
early 1950s).
NMM

3 Fast motor gunboat (Head Office plan
23370, 9 October 1940).
NMM

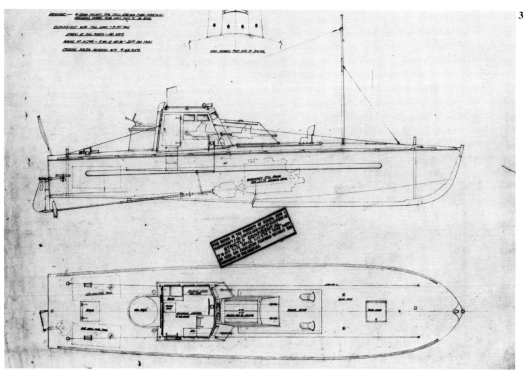

ATTACK & DEFENCE No4

Action Damage to British Warships in the Second World War Part 2

By David Brown RCNC

BOMBS

There are so many sizes and types of bomb that it is difficult to tell a connected story. In the Second World War, high capacity bombs, exploding in the superstructure, might cause comparatively little damage while medium case bombs, penetrating deep into the ship, would cause severe structural damage as well as flooding and fire.

The great story of survival is that of the carrier *Illustrious* in January 1941, attacked by Ju 87 dive bombers near Malta (Ref 1). On the 10th she was hit by seven bombs and near missed by another, probably all 500kg (1100lb) weapons. The following hits were recorded:

1 On S2 pompom (starboard side). The gun was destroyed but little other damage was caused.
2 Pierced the forward end of the flight deck, went out of the ship and exploded near the waterline causing extensive splinter damage (resulting in some flooding) and a small fire.
3 Hit in the after lift well and severely damaged the lift and its machinery.
4 Penetrated the 3in thick flight deck armour and burst in the hangar, causing serious damage to the forward lift and a bad fire in the hangar. (Some accounts claim that this was a 1000kg/2200lb bomb.) Several aircraft were destroyed in the hangar.
5 Direct hit at the aft end of the after lift.
6 Passed through P1 pompom platform and went into the sea without exploding. Fire started in two mess decks.
7 Hit in the after lift well (possibly a smaller bomb).
8 Near miss off starboard side with slight flooding.

With the steering gear out of action, *Illustrious* returned to Malta steering on her main engines. While she was being repaired she suffered damage from two more 500kg bombs. The first hit the unarmoured after end of the flight deck and exploded above the gallery deck, while the other was a near miss, off the port side, which flooded some of the torpedo protection compartments and caused shock damage to the port boiler and machinery. After all this, HMS *Illustrious* proceeded to Alexandria under her own power at 23kts. Repairs took 6 months in Norfolk Navy Yard, USA. It is interesting to note that the armoured hangar, provided at such great expense, proved of no value. Only one bomb hit the armour and that penetrated the 3in deck (see *Warship* 13). The ship was also lucky in that

several hits were close together so that the later ones added little to the earlier damage. On the other hand, to withstand 8 hits and 2 near misses from 500kg bombs was a great achievement. Her designer, W A D Forbes, Captain Boyd and the crew all had reason for pride in their work.

Bomb hits on thick armour were very few, the best known being on 9 April 1940 when the battleship *Rodney* was hit by a delayed action (DA) bomb, believed to have been a 500kg AP type. After piercing the upper and main decks between the funnel and bridge it broke up while penetrating the 4in armour of the middle deck. There was a partial detonation and minor damage was caused by blast and splinters.

Bombs were a much greater hazard to small ships – Table 1 (see Part 1, *Warship* 27) shows that 44 destroyers were sunk by these weapons and 81 seriously damaged. Even quite small bombs could cause major damage. The destroyer *Vanessa* was hit by a 100kg bomb in June 1941 while operating in the North Sea. It entered through the side at the top of No 1 boiler room and burst near the bottom. The outer bottom was pushed upwards over the whole length of the boiler room and for some distance forward, and a hole 6ft × 9ft blown in the bottom. The upper deck was split and blown upwards, and the forward funnel blown overboard. Both boiler rooms were flooded. Repairs took 9 months including conversion to escort.

GUIDED WEAPONS, ETC

There were comparatively few guided weapons used in the war and their effects were very similar to those of bombs. The sloop *Egret* was hit by an HS 293 glider bomb off Spain on 28 August 1943. The hit was high up on the starboard side near the funnel, she capsized one minute later and sank an hour and a quarter after that. It seems likely that a magazine also exploded. The cruiser *Spartan* was also sunk by this weapon while off Anzio on 29 January 1944. A large hole was blown in the upper deck and a serious fire broke out in the after superstructure and in Y turret. The after engine room was evacuated and the after magazine flooded about ten minutes after the hit. One hour later the ship was abandoned and sank soon after.

Earlier, the battleship *Warspite* survived a hit and a near miss from 1400kg FX 1400 guided bombs (11 September 1943). The hit was on the boat deck, the bomb penetrating to the double bottom before explod-

HMS Cameron capsized in dock following damage from a 250kg (551lb) direct action bomb on 5 December 1940. The ship was out of action for 17 months but this included a 10½ month conversion into an experimental ship.

MoD

ing, producing a a hole some 20ft × 14ft in the outer bottom and wrecking No 4 boiler room. The main bulkheads forward and aft of the boiler room were buckled and torn. The near miss exploded under the bulge abreast No 5 boiler room and flooded No 2, 3, 5 and 6 boiler rooms and other spaces. She was repaired sufficiently to join the Fleet off Normandy in June 1944 but still had a hole in her bottom.

Japanese suicide bombers were a form of guided missile. Hits on the carriers of the British Pacific Fleet are summarised in Table 3.

The County class cruiser *Australia* seemed to have a special attraction for suicidal Japanese. She was hit on 21 October 1944, when serious fires broke out in the bridge area due to burning petrol. She was hit again on 5 January 1945 and remained in action with damage to her AA guns. She was hit again the next day with more

The result of a direct bomb hit on the stern of the destroyer *Acheron* on 24 August 1940. She was also damaged by 3 near misses and was out of action for 13 weeks.

MoD

damage and casualties to the AA guns and crew. On 8 January she was hit by two more aircraft and yet again on the 9th. She was still able to steam at reduced speed and was repaired and refitted in 6½ weeks.

TABLE 3: EFFECTS OF KAMIKAZE ATTACKS

Ship	Date	No of hits	Time out of action	Repair time	Notes
Indefatigable	1 April 1945	1	50mins	1 month	Zeke with 250kg bomb.
Illustrious	6 April 1945	1	–	–	Glancing blow.
Formidable	4 May 1945	1	5 hours	–	Zeke with 250kg bomb, hole in armoured flight deck.
Indomitable	4 May 1945	1	–	–	8 planes lost, 8k, 51w.
Victorious	9 May 1945	2	(Fly off 1 hour) (Fly on 12 hours)	1 month	
Formidable	9 May 1945	1	25 minutes	1month	9 planes lost, 1k, 8w.

GUNFIRE

Damage from shells is even more variable in extent. The bursting charge is small and serious damage will only occur if a vital space is struck. The damage received by the battleship *Prince of Wales* in action with *Bismarck* and *Prinz Eugen* on 24 May 1941 well illustrates the random nature of damage due to shell hits. The hits and their effects were:

1 A 15in shell which hit the compass platform and passed out without exploding. Damage to the ship was negligible but most of the bridge crew were killed or incapacitated leading to a temporary loss of control.

2 A 15in shell struck the starboard crane and burst just abaft the after funnel causing extensive minor splinter damage. A radar office was put out of action.

3 A 15in shell hit 28ft below the waterline on the starboard side which penetrated the outer torpedo protection and came to rest, without exploding, against the protective bulkhead. There was some flooding.

4 An 8in shell (from *Prinz Eugen*) pierced the boat deck, shelter deck and the armoured structure round P3 5.25in turret, bounced off and came to rest without exploding. The gun mount was temporarily out of action.

5 An 8in shell hit the starboard side just below the waterline and partially detonated 11ft inboard. The lower deck was flooded for 60ft and there was minor splinter and blast damage.

6 An 8in shell burst on impact with the side 5ft below the waterline over the steering gear. The armour deck was distorted and there was flooding at lower deck level for 80ft.

7 An 8in shell hit the director support on the bridge, put both HA directors out of action and passed on without exploding.

That only two shells out of seven detonated does not say much for the quality of German fuzes. On the other hand, flooding and minor damage was quite extensive and, had the shells exploded properly, *Prince of Wales* would have been seriously damaged.

The cruiser *Berwick* had an exciting time at the end of 1940. On 27 November she was in action with the Italian Fleet off Cape Spartivento in the Mediterranean and was hit by two 8in shells. The first hit and penetrated the 1in thick support to 'Y' turret and burst in a cabin flat after travelling 21ft. There was only minor structural damage and a small fire. The second shell hit the upper deck, which it penetrated, together with the main and lower decks and burst after a path of 40ft outside 'Y' turret handing room. The electrical ring main was cut and all lights went out in the after end of the ship. Other than that, damage was slight. *Berwick*'s fighting efficiency was not impaired except that 'Y' turret was out of action.

Temporary repairs took 20 days and, on Christmas Day, she was successfully defending a large troop convoy against the German cruiser *Hipper* off the Azores, suffering four hits from 8in shells. One hit the side of 'X' turret and passed through the floor and support without exploding. The turret was jammed. One hit the side and penetrated the platform deck, bouncing off various sections of structure before coming to rest in a fuel tank without exploding. There was some flooding. The third hit of the engagement was on a 4in AA mounting. The shell was deflected and exploded in a funnel uptake 56ft later, after passing through several bulkheads. Damage was slight. The last hit was on 4½in thick 'C' armour which deflected the shell into the bulge where it exploded. A 40ft length of bulge was flooded.

Damage to the bows of the destroyer *Whitshed* after she struck a contact mine on 30 July 1940; she was out of action for 19 weeks.
MoD

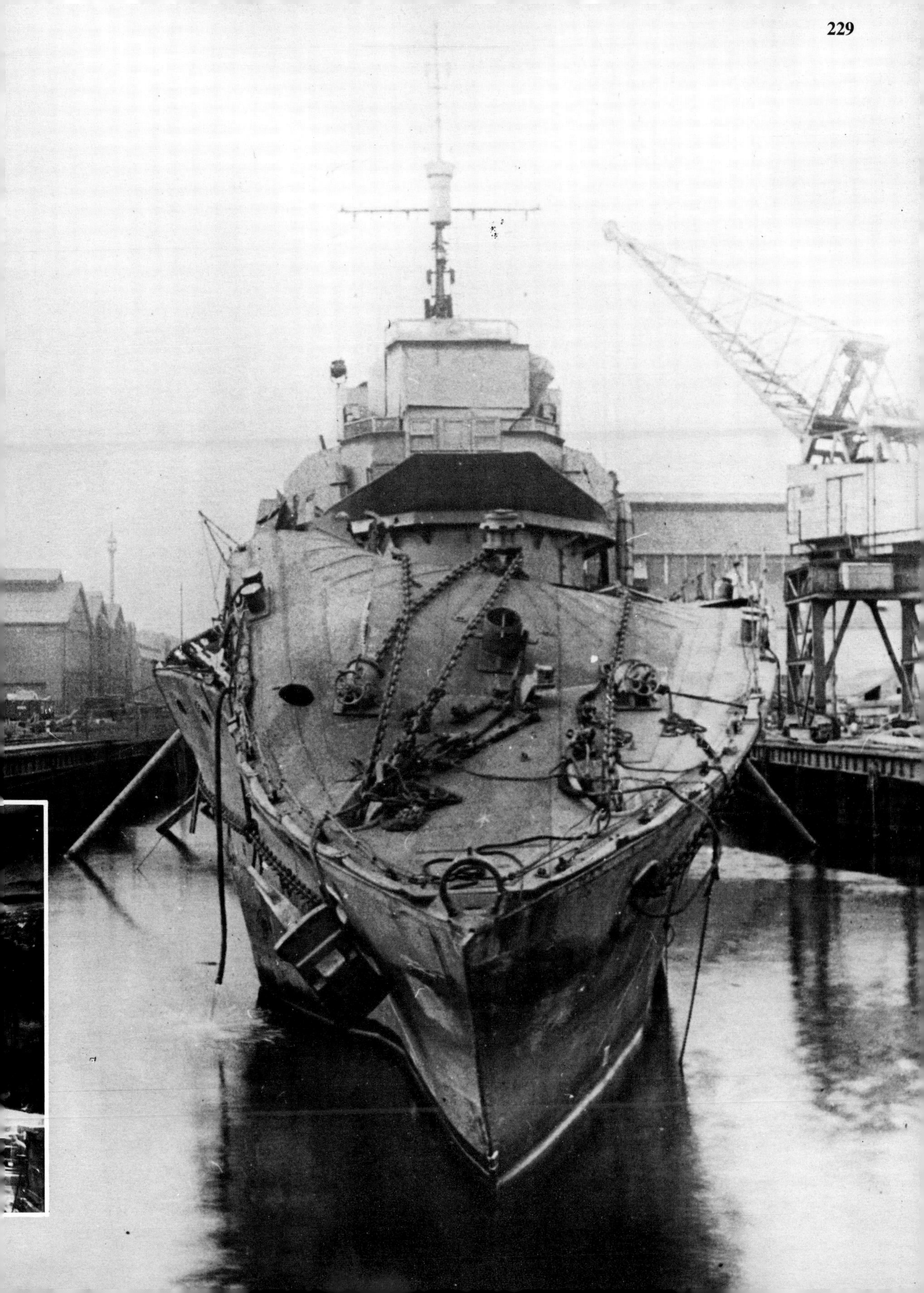

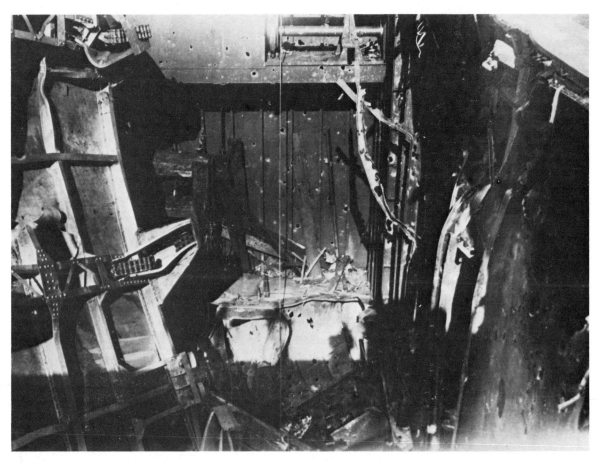

Damage to the after lift of the carrier *Illustrious* caused by a bomb hit on 10 January 1941. The lift platform is on the left!
MoD

Other than the loss of 'X' turret, *Berwick* was in good fighting order. Repairs took 6 months. Once again, poor German fuzes saved her from more serious damage but, even so, she stood up well to shell fire – as indeed did her near sister *Norfolk* when hit by two 11in shells from *Scharnhorst*.

Hipper was in action again in the Barents Sea, 31 December 1942, when she scored three 8in hits on the destroyer *Onslow*. The first hit the funnel and caused very extensive splinter damage – two radars, an Oerlikon and the aerials were wrecked and both boilers damaged. The second shell exploded on the sheer strake between 'A' and 'B' guns, making a hole 6ft × 5ft. Extensive splinter damage was again caused wrecking the main cable runs and 'A' gun barrel, and starting a serious fire. The last hit was on 'B' gun deck making a hole 6ft × 4ft in the superstructure and wrecking 'B' gun. There was also a near miss close to 'B' gun which caused further minor splinter damage. Though the for-ward guns were both out of action, *Onslow* was still able to steam and use the after guns.

MINES
Contact mines make a big hole similar to that caused by a torpedo. In many cases the damage was forward and even when severe the remains could be brought home and repaired.

Damage caused by ground mines was of a very different character. There was shock damage (usually throughout the ship), whipping (which might cause major buckling of the structure) and flooding (through strained seams, ruptured plating or cracked fillings). The cruiser *Belfast* was one of the early victims of a magnetic mine, in the Firth of Forth on 21 November 1939 (Ref 1). The mine exploded 80 – 90ft below the forward engine room causing severe structural damage to the bridge, upper deck and keel – the whole ship was bent upwards through 4½ft.

Despite this damage there was only slight flooding. On the other hand, there was extensive damage to weapons, machinery and electrical equipmemt and all their supporting seats were broken. In most cases, these were of cast iron which is very brittle under shock loading. Repairs to *Belfast* were carried out in Devonport Dockyard at low priority and took two years to complete.

Shock damage had been studied before the war in Job 74 (see *Warship* 24) but the short length of this target did not allow whipping acceleration to develop nor were the charges used as big as those in the mine used against *Belfast*. Improvements were made as quickly as possible with better materials, flexible mounts and equipments designed without overhanging masses. The failure to protect properly against shock was the biggest fault in pre-war warship design – not only in British ships but also in those of all other naval powers. Nearly 5 years after the mining of *Belfast*, the German battleship *Tir-*

pitz was similarly immobilised by shock damage caused by the midget submarine attack on her.

CONCLUSION

The study of damage from enemy weapons was taken very seriously by all concerned: the DNC, Sir Stanley Goodall, would usually interview the survivors from major incidents himself. Continual attention to detail in the design of pipe systems, cables and switchgear gradually improved the survivability of ships. The provision of more battery powered emergency lights and of portable pumps helped the crews to control the effects of damage. A damage control school was set up in London in 1942 at which training was given in all aspects of the subject. Flooding, counter-flooding and stability was taught using a large model of the cruiser HMS *London* floating in a big tank.

The fact remains that weapons are meant to cause serious damage and it need cause no surprise that such damage did result. One is inclined to wonder if the massive investment in armour and in torpedo protection

The wrecked stern of the sloop *Pelican* after a direct hit by a 250lb direct action bomb on 22 April 1940. The stern section abaft Y mounting has gone together with the mounting shield. She was also damaged by two 250lb near miss bombs and was out of action for 7 months.

MoD

What is left of the fore end of the destroyer *Express* is almost unrecognisable in this view of the ship after striking a contact mine on 31 August 1940.

systems was justified. Even a Second World War ship had so many vital systems outside the protected area that the ship could be put out of action without the protection being penetrated. Weapon development was so rapid that the protection itself was likely to become inadequate quite quickly.

Many of the incidents of the war could not be fully documented either because the ship sank or because the crew were too busy. Gaps in knowledge were filled after the war when a considerable number of old ships were used for trials of weapon effectiveness before they were broken up (Ref 1).

Both designers and operators learnt much from the hard experience of war and improvements were made to equipment and to training but the Fleet which went to war in 1939 was basically sound.

REFERENCES

1 *A Century of Naval Construction* D K Brown (Conway Maritime Press, 1983.)
2 *US Destroyers* N Friedman, (US Naval Institute Press, 1982.)
3 *British Destroyers* E J March, (Seeley Service & Co, 1966.)

WARSHIP PICTORIAL

America's First Submarines Part 2

By Francis J Allen

Brief Histories of Classes and Ships

With the commissioning of the *Holland* on 12 October 1900 the service career of the submarine designed by John P Holland and built by Lewis Nixon (the designer of the battleships *Oregon, Indiana* and *Massachusetts*) in his Crescent Shipyard began somewhat ignominiously with the boat having to be towed, by the tug *Leyden*, to the Naval Academy at Annapolis, Maryland on 16 October 1900. At Annapolis the *Holland* assumed training duties for the preparation of naval cadets, officers and enlisted men for duty in the fledgling submarine service. *Holland*'s service record was one of experimentation and training. During 8–10 January 1901 she travelled from Annapolis, Maryland to Norfolk, Virginia, a distance of 166 miles, running on the surface; in the process collecting valuable data for use in future submarines. With the exception of a period from 15 June to 1 October 1901, when the *Holland* was stationed at the Naval Torpedo Station at Newport, RI, she remained at the Naval Academy until 17 July 1905 as a training vessel.

Holland's name was struck from the Navy Register of Ships on 21 November 1910 after completing her service career at Norfolk, Virginia. A Henry A Hitner & Sons of Philadelphia purchased her for scrap in June 1913. The sale was made with the understanding that the purchaser was to put up a $5000 bond to guarantee that the ship would be broken up and not used as a warship.

With the advent of the *Adder* Class, later to be redesigned as the A-Class, the submarine fleet of the United States Navy was born. The contract covering these six boats called for their delivery between 1902 and early 1903. The submarines *Adder* (A-2), *Moccasin* (A-4), *Porpoise* (A-6) and *Shark* (A-7) were built by Lewis Nixon at the Crescent Shipyard in Elizabethport, NJ while *Grampus* (A-3), and *Pike* (A-5) were constructed at the Union Iron Works in San Francisco, California. *Plunger* (A-1), ordered under a separate contract, was also built at the Crescent Shipyard. As the boats were completed they were taken to the Holland Torpedo Boat Company's station at Cutchogue Bay for tests and trials. This station at the Goldsmith and Tuttell Yard in New Suffolk soon became a semi-official submarine base for the US Navy. On the West Coast the tests and trials were carried out at the Union Iron Works.

For the most part, the work assigned to these first submarines was concerned with the development of suitable tactics and the training of personnel for these and future boats. All the A-Class were employed in this fashion for the first part of their service careers.

With the exception of *Plunger*, the A-Class boats served their most important duty with the 1st Submarine Division, Asiatic Torpedo Fleet in the waters off Cavite, Luzon, Philippine Islands. The first two of the A-Class, *Porpoise* and *Shark*, arrived aboard *Caesar* (AC-16) and both were in service by November and August 1908 respectively. *Adder* and *Moccasin* were also transported to the Philippine Islands on board *Caesar* and both of these boats were recommissioned by October 1909. The last two A-Class submarines, *Grampus* and *Pike* were operational in March 1915, having arrived on the transport *Hector* (AC-7). They remained in the Philippines through the First World War and for the remainder of their operational careers ending their service as targets and/or being sold for scrap. On 16 January 1922 all of the A-Class boats, with the exception of A-1, were stricken from the Navy List. *Plunger*'s name was stricken on 24 February 1913.

In terms of naval architecture the early submarines and those of today have some strong links. Much experimentation, trial and error has passed over and about them in the intervening years, but the links are still there. The principal link which binds the old boats, considered good only to assist fixed land fortifications in harbour defence, to the modern submarine is the ingenuity and resourcefulness of the men who built, crewed and commanded them.

1

2

1 USS *Ajax* (AC-14) in Manila Bay, PI, after transporting submarines *B2* and *B3* (SS–11 and SS–12) from Norfolk. Taken in late April or early May 1913.
USN

2 The switchboard and other controls of the *A4* (SS-5) taken at Manila *c* 1912.
USN

3 USS *Grampus* (SS-4) off San Diego, California, 1910.
USN

3

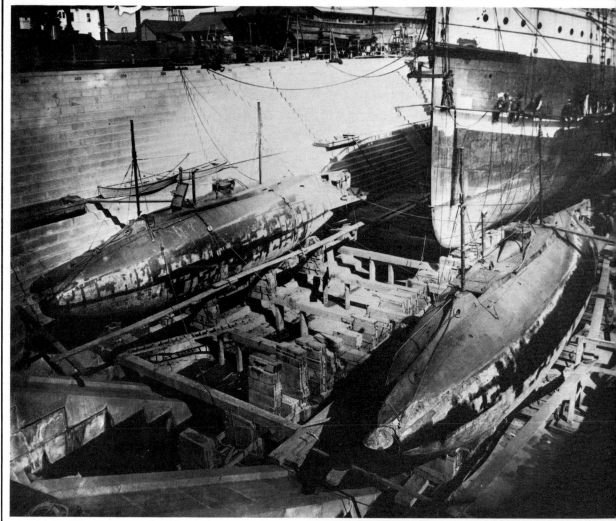

USS *Grampus* (SS-4), USS *Pike* (SS-6) and troop transport *Lawton* in drydock at Mare Island Navy Yard, California, September 1906.

USN

Submarines *A6* (SS-7), *A4* (SS-5) and *A2* (SS-3) in the Dewey Drydock, Olongapo Naval Station, PI, *c* 1912. The bows of the submarine tender *Mohican* (1883-1922) are on the left, with anchor suspended from cathead.

USN

USS *A2* (SS-3) loading a torpedo, at Cavite Navy Yard, PI *c*1912.
USN

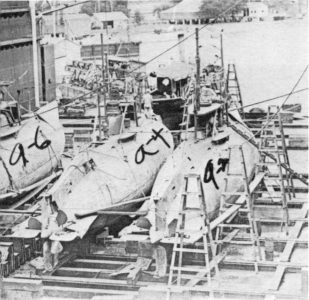

3

4

1 Left to right: USS *B1*, USS *A7*, *c*1920, probably in the Philippines.
USN

2 USS *A7* (SS-8) at the Cavite Navy Yard PI, prior to the First World War.
USN

3 USS *Adder* (SS-3) running trials, *c*1903.
USN

4 USS *A2* (SS-3) underway in Manila Bay, *c*1912.
USN

5 USS *Plunger* (SS-2) *c*1909. The photograph has been signed by the future Admiral Chester W Nimitz, who was her third commanding officer.
USN

5

British Naval Guns 1880-1945 No 11

By NJM Campbell

6in QF Mks I and II These guns differed in construction only and are listed together in nearly all armament lists. Separate ammunition was fired. Mk I, first ordered in May 1888, was EOC Pattern 'Z' and was of built up construction, the principal components being 'A' tube, breech piece, '1B' and '2B' tubes, 'C' tube and jacket, while Mk II was a Woolwich design with 'A' tube, '1B' tube, 'B' hoop, '2B' tube, wire over the '1B' tube (c40% of total length) and jacket. Both had the '2B' tube extending to the muzzle and screw breech blocks with, originally, 3-motion breech mechanism (BM). Most were later converted to single motion BM, indicated by the addition of the letter 'B' to the mark number. One reference has been found to Mk II* which is thought to refer to the addition of a cartridge retaining catch when used as an AA gun.

In the latter part of the First World War, 15 guns of the same general design as the British type, were sent by Japan but they were never mounted afloat. Altogether 137 Mk I and 760 Mk II guns were made of which 133 and 714 respectively were naval and the rest coast defence.

Mks I and II were mounted in the battleships of the *Royal Sovereign* class, *Hood, Renown, Majestic* class, *Canopus* class and rearmed *Nile* class and *Superb*. Of large cruisers they were mounted in the *Edgar* class to the *Diadem* class inclusive, and also as upper deck guns in the rearmed *Blake* class. Smaller cruisers comprised *Aeolus, Brilliant, Iphigenia* and the *Astraea* to the *Highflyer* classes inclusive, as well as the rearmed *Indefatigable, Intrepid* and later *Rainbow* and *Sirius*. In addition they were added to the old battleship *Hercules* and the cruisers *Immortalité* and *Narcissus* and various gunnery school gunboats.

During the First World War they were at one time or another in all the large monitors except *Abercrombie, Havelock, Raglan, Peterborough* and *Picton*, and also in the small monitors *M26, M27* and the *Aphis* class river gunboats as well as in many AMCs and DAMS; 63 Mk II guns were transferred to the Army for conversion to 8in howitzers.

The mountings were CPI and PII allowing 20° and 19° elevation respectively in the upper deck version, and 15° for both in the between deck version. Originally CPI was in the *Royal Sovereign* class and *Hood*, and in the cruisers of the *Blake, Edgar, Crescent*, the 5 *Aeolus* (not *Rainbow, Sirius*) and *Astraea* classes, but there were some changes later. PII* applied to a First World War

EOC conversion with a new cradle allowing 25° elevation, but none of the 40 made were put afloat. Four CPI and 12 PII were adapted by AA use in 1915-16 with up to $53\frac{1}{2}$° elevation, but they were not very successful, though a CPI conversion was fitted in *Roberts* and a PII in the river gunboats *Cicala, Cockchafer, Cricket* and *Glowworm* when stationed on the East Coast as defence against Zeppelins. The remaining mountings were used on land, with the PII on railway trucks.

6in QF Mk III This was a trunnioned version of Mk I, known to EOC as Pattern Z^1, intended for Vavasseur mountings and mounted in VCP Mk IIC or II*, both of which allowed 20° elevation. A total of 53 guns were made and used as the main deck guns in the rearmed *Blake*, and *Apollo* classes except for *Aeolus, Brilliant, Iphigenia, Indefatigable* and *Intrepid* of the latter. About 8 were later in DAMS.

6in BL Mks VII, VIII The only difference between these was that Mk VIII had the breech opening to the left to suit the left hand guns in the twin turrets of the *Kent* class cruisers. The guns were designed by Vickers and became one of the main standbys of both the Navy and Army,

Profile of the PVI mounting for the Mk XI 6in gun, mounted in the *Weymouth* and *Chatham* class cruisers of the First World War.
Drawn by John Roberts

though originally there was some trouble. They were built with an inner 'A' tube, 'A' tube, wire for about half length and 'B' tube to the muzzle, jacket and screwed-on breech ring. The breech bush taking the Welin screw block, was located in the 'A' tube. Mk VIIv comprised 12 Army guns with no 'B' tube, and VII* and VIIv* were guns relined with a high strength alloy steel inner 'A' tube to allow heavier charges in the later 45° coast defence mountings. Although there were 928 naval guns; 898 Mk VII, 27 Mk VIII and 3 converted from Mk VIII to VII. The total number of Army guns is not known but was probably about 350 with, in addition, many transferred from the Navy.

The gun was capable of a much higher performance than was accepted for reasons of standardisation in most, where the muzzle velocity was that required by a notoriously bad driving band and a coast defence mounting with a cast iron pedestal. Mk VII was mounted in the battleships of the *Formidable*, *London* and *Duncan* classes, the first 5 *King Edwards*, the *Iron Duke* class and the battlecruiser *Tiger*, as well as in the rearmed *Barfleur* class battleships. Cruisers included the *Cressy*, *Drake*, *Kent*, *Hampshire* and *Challenger* classes, and some rearmed ships including *Narcissus*, *Immortalité*, *Undaunted*, *Endymion*, *Theseus*, *Edgar*, *Grafton*, *High-flyer*, *Hyacinth*, *Vindictive*, and all the *Dido* class except *Eclipse*, *Astraea*, *Fox*, *Amethyst*, *Adventure* and *Atten-tive*. Other warships comprised the 12in monitors except *Peterborough* and *Picton*, the monitor *M27* and the *Humber* class, the gunboats of the *Aphis* class except *Ladybird*, the leader *Swift* and briefly the destroyer *Viking*. It was also in the school gunboats *Bustard*, *Cuckoo* and *Drudge*, the 1919 Caspian Force and Siberia River Flotilla, many AMC and other auxiliary warships in both World Wars, some DAMS and many DEMS. Apart from the *Kent* class, Mk VIII was only in the *Drudge* and the First World War escort ship *Discoverer*.

On land Mk VII was mainly a coast defence gun though it was used as a heavy field gun in the First World War and a few were on railway trucks in the second.

Most naval guns fired charges to give the standard 2562–2573fs muzzle velocity but heavier charges to give 2770–2775fs were used by the 5 *King Edwards*, the *Iron Duke* class, *Tiger*, the *Hampshire* class and *Swift*. The gunboats *Aphis*, *Cockchafer* and *Scarab* also had these heavier charges in the Second World War, as did the AMCs *Alcantara*, *Carnarvon Castle*, *Cheshire* and *Worcestershire* but with 112lb, 6crh shells and 2640fs MV. No ship had the charges for 2890fs used in Mk VII* and VIIv* guns.

The *Kent* class had Mk I (Vickers) or Mk II (EOC) twin turrets with PIII or PIV single mountings which were in nearly all other ships, though the *Iron Duke* class and *Tiger* had PVIII as did some Second World War

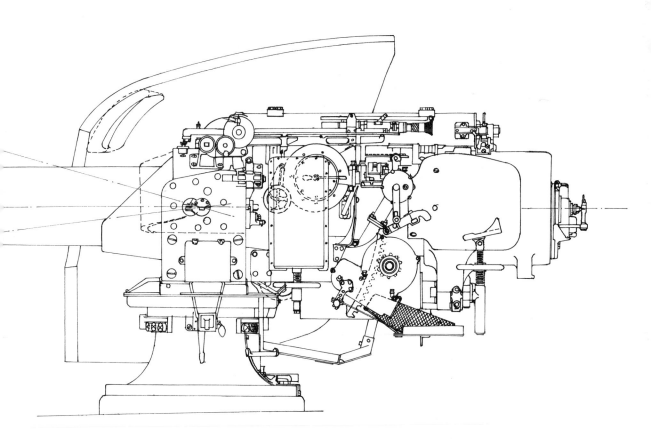

auxiliaries. Elevation was 14° in PVIII and 15° in other mountings, though this was later often increased to 20° in PIII and IV.

6in BL Mks IX, X Only one of each of these 49.8 calibre experimental coast defence guns was made. They were of built up construction differing in the breech blocks, and were respectively EOC Pattern DD¹ and DD², being BL versions of the QF Pattern DD mounted in the Brazilian *Barroso* and US *Albany* and *New Orleans*. With a 100lb shell MV is variously given as 2498 and 2575fs.

6in BL Mk XI Guns of wire wound type with inner 'A' tube, 'A' tube, full length wire, 'B' tube, jacket and screwed on breech ring. The breech bush taking the Welin block, screwed into the 'A' tube. Mk XI* differed in having a thicker inner 'A' with cannelured rings at the two forward shoulders. Of the 177 guns, all naval, 34 were Mk XI, 18 Mk XI* and 124 Mk XI* with a slightly different breech ring to suit PVI mountings, though all would go in PV or PV*. Lastly 'H' XI* was a Coventry

ordnance stock gun with Holmstrom BM, eventually linered to an experimental 3in and never mounted afloat. There were slight constructional differences in various guns but with no alteration in mark.

The guns were in PV mountings in the battleships *Africa*, *Britannia* and *Hibernia*, and the cruisers *Black Prince* and *Duke of Edinburgh*, in PV* in the *Bristol* class cruisers, and in PVI in the *Falmouth* and *Chatham* class cruisers. Subsequently they were in the monitors *Marshal Ney*, the *Protector*, some First World War AMCs and a few other ships including DAMS. In the Second World War they were in Ocean Boarding Vessels and some DEMS. They were also mounted as emergency coast defence guns in the Second World War and to a limited extent in the First, while guns from the Australian ships of the *Chatham* class were installed on land in Australia during the 1930s.

PV and V* mountings allowed 13° elevation, later 20° in some, and PVI 15°. The guns were found heavy to aim manually, particularly in the *Falmouth* class which were lively in a seaway, and hydraulic power gear was added to some in the latter part of the First World War.

PARTICULARS OF 6IN GUNS

	6in QF Mk I, II, III	6in BL Mk VII, VIII	6in BL Mk XI
Weight incl. BM (tons):	6.6 (Mk III 6.75)	7.398	8.588
Length oa (in):	249.25	279.228	309.728
Length bore (cals):	40	44.92	50
Chamber (cu in):	832	1715	2030
Chamber length (in):	23.65	32.74	34.3
Projectile (lb):	100	100	100
Charge (ib/type):	29.75/EXE	20/Cord 20	32.1/MD26
	13.25/Cord 30	23/MD16	33.05/SC 150
	15.94/MD 26	23.13/SC 103	
		28.63/MD 26	
		28.17/SC140	
Muzzle Velocity (fs):	1882 EXE	2536 Cord	2937
	2230 Cord	2562 MD	
	2243 MD	2573	
		2770 MD	
		2775 SC	
Range (yds)/elevation:	10,000/15° (2crh Cord)	14600/20° (4crh SC)	14310/15° (4crh)
		15800/20° (4crh SC)	

Loading practice with a 6in Mk XII aboard a C class cruiser in 1935
MoD

USS KEOKUK

By S Kirby

This, and the other photographs accompanying this article, show the author's excellent model of the *USS Keokuk*.

All photos author's collection

Keokuk was the leader of the Sauk Indian tribe in the early 1800s. His name means 'one who moves about alert' or 'Running Fox'. I wonder what he would have made of the rather useless warship that was to bear his name?

Charles W Whitney was obviously a naval architect with an imaginative mind. His theories were so quite different from those of John Ericsson that the naval authorities must have wondered for some time who was right! Ericsson's main principle was to submerge the main part of the ship almost out of sight, leaving only the turret and pilot house above water level. This resulted in a very small target, but had the great disadvantage of providing very little reserve buoyancy. This small reserve was lost in deep water off Cape Hatteras, below which the *Monitor* still lies!

Whitney gave his vessel *Keokuk*, a much greater reserve buoyancy, but this obviously meant a much

Keokuk viewed from ahead. Note the hull form, ram bow and the grating which formed the roof of the 'fixed' gunhouses.

larger target. The basic design was very advanced, in that the vessel had a central citadel of angled armour with unarmoured, floodable ends. The armour itself is interesting in that it comprised alternate 4in × 4in beams of wood and iron set on edge and running horizontally along the length of the ship. *Keokuk* was armed with two 11in Dahlgren smoothbores.

Whitney submitted the specifications for his design on 22 April 1861. The principal dimensions were to be: length 150ft; beam 30ft; draft 8ft; and displacement 1,497,600lb (668 tons).

For some reason the go-ahead was not given until nearly a year later on 18 March 1862, by which time *Monitor* had been built and had had her rather inconclusive battle with *Virginia*. I am not convinced that the Navy were really happy with *Monitor*, otherwise why did they accept a design that was the complete antithesis of the Ericsson concept? Perhaps due to a shortage of ships the Navy was just making use of an existing design to save time. The cost of $220,000 compared with *Monitor*'s $275,000 must have made *Keokuk* seem fair value for money, bearing in mind they were identically armed. At this stage Whitney's 'Iron Mail' Clad Floating Battery or Steam Gun-Boat was to be called *Moodna* and her keel was laid on 14 April 1862 at J S Underhill's Iron Works, East River, New York.

HULL STRUCTURE

The basic hull structure was of 4in × $\frac{3}{4}$in iron bar frames at 18in spacing, with five keelsons constructed of 20in deep by $\frac{1}{2}$in thick iron sheet capped with $3\frac{1}{2}$in × $2\frac{1}{2}$in × $\frac{7}{16}$in angle bar. The hull was subdivided by three transverse hulkheads, one each 20ft from the hull extremities and the third just forward of the boilers. The bulkheads were $\frac{3}{8}$in sheet stiffened with 3in × 3in × $\frac{7}{8}$in angles set vertically and 30in apart.

The hull plating was $\frac{7}{16}$in Best American Boiler plate . . . put on in outside and inside courses[1] . . . up to a line 3ft below the waterline, the rest to be butt-jointed, yielding a smooth surface over which the 'shot-proof mail'[1] or armour would be laid.

The unusual arrangement of this armour was described by Whitney in a letter to Rear Admiral Samuel F DuPont, commanding the blockade of Charleston, on 24 April 1863: 'The apparent thickness of the armour on the sides of *Keokuk* was $5\frac{3}{4}$in, put on in a peculiar manner, viz: bars of iron 4in wide and 1in thick were placed edgewise over the skin of the ship running fore and aft, 1in apart, and between them were placed strips of wood of the same dimensions; over this were laid two plates of iron each $\frac{5}{8}$in thick secured on the edges of the bars by $1\frac{1}{8}$in bolts running between them and through the skin and fastened by a nut on the inside of the vessel.'

The captain on his bridge – the roof of the forward gunhouse.

The gun-houses or towers were originally to be diamond shaped, but were later changed to truncated round cones 14ft in diameter on top and 20ft at the base. The tops were covered by a grating for light and ventilation. Each tower had three gun-ports, one on each beam and a third on the centre line bearing either ahead or astern as appropriate to the fore and aft tower. The ports were covered by 4½in thick iron doors or stoppers. Each door was in two parts, these being opened by levers and tackles inside the tower and were designed to close themselves when the gun was fired. This was apparently achieved by letting the split doors rest on the gun barrel when in its 'run-out' position. They then closed themselves as the barrel recoiled into the tower!

The guns were 11in Dahlgren smooth bores mounted on slides, the whole gun and mounting assembly being mounted on a turntable within the tower. The arcs of fire must have been very restricted by the three small ports. The armour on the gun-towers was similar to that on the sides of the ship, but with an extra ½in plate all over.

Whitney's attention to detail led him to realise the danger of the armour-retaining bolts sustaining sheared heads and being driven through into the gun-tower. He overcame this problem by fitting *Keokuk* with 'an inner skin protecting those inside the turrets and pilot house against the flying of the bolts'.

The pilot house was in the form of a bustle on the rear of, and slightly higher than, the forward gun-tower. Slits with sliding shutters on the forward face enabled the helmsman to see ahead.

MACHINERY

The machinery comprised two engines, each of two cylinders with a 23in bore and 20in stroke. The cylinders were vertical and drove the shafts *beside* the cylinders via a system of cranks and links. The result was a complex but compact engine that later proved quite reliable. Each engine drove a four bladed propeller of 7ft 6in diameter and 13ft 6in pitch. Steam was provided by two cylindrical boilers working at 60psi and a total of 400hp was developed. Whitney guaranteed a speed of 10kts, but most references quote 9kts as the speed she finally achieved. Whitney cunningly glossed over this shortfall by proudly stating in his letter to Admiral DuPont 'She was designed to have a speed and she attained it, running out of New York Harbor at the rate of 10 miles an hour' That's almost exactly 9kts to the uninitiated!

The floodable ends of the vessel were filled and emptied by steam driven pumps. The main function is quoted in the specification to be a trimming system to enable the vessel's optimum waterline to be maintained regardless of the amount of coal, ammunition and stores carried. The Captain of the vessel seemed to think that the intention was to fill these reservoirs completely to form 'water armour'. This would undoubtedly have added considerably to *Keokuk's* displacement, but careful perusal of all available notes has not revealed whether the displacement draft quoted is with the ends full or empty.

Although named *Woodna* when the keel was laid, she had been renamed *Keokuk* by the time Mrs Whitney, the designer's wife, officially launched the vessel on 6 December 1862. The principal dimensions by this time were: length 159½ft (over ram and rudder); beam 36ft; draft 8ft forward, 9ft aft; and displacement around 677 tons.

PREPARATION FOR BATTLE

On 24 February the following year *Keokuk* was commissioned with Cdr Alexander C Rhind in command. On 11 March she left New York to join the South Atlantic Blockading Squadron and arrived at Newport News on the 13th to prepare for a planned attack on Charleston. She left on the 17th and after a short delay to repair a damaged propeller, arrived off South Carolina on 26 March. Rear Admiral DuPont was in command of the squadron at that time but he did not have the confidence that Secretary of the Navy Gideon Welles had that his ships could successfully take on and beat the coastal forts on the approaches to Charleston. Welles strongly urged DuPont to attack and, as this virtually amounted to an order, DuPont had no choice.

So on 4 April he reluctantly issued an order to sail up the main channel towards Charleston and attack Fort Sumter when within easy range. The ships were to shoot from the NE at 600–800yds range and to direct their fire at the central embrasure. They were instructed to take their time to ensure accuracy and not to waste ammunition.

The vessels concerned were the monitor-types *Weehawken*, *Passaic*, *Montauk*, *Patapsco*, *Catskill*, *Nantucket* and *Nahant* along with the gunboat *Keokuk*. DuPont was aboard his flagship *New Ironside*. A follow-up force of wooden gunboats *Canandaigua*, *Housatonic*, *Huron*, *Unadilla* and *Wissahickton* was to join the main squadron in an attack on the Morris Island batteries following the destruction of Fort Sumter.

This basic plan gives some idea of the misplaced optimism of Welles. On the other hand it may have been that DuPont, knowing something of King Canute's activities, put forward this over-ambitious plan to prove it could not be done; like holding back the incoming tide!

The attack was to take place on the morning of 6 April 1863. The squadron formed up off North Edisto Island near Port Royal and reached the Charleston bar late in the morning of 5 April and moored about 6 miles from Fort Sumter. *Keokuk* and *Patapsco* were detailed to mark the bar with buoys and then to stay with them just inside the bar opposite the remainder of the squadron, still outside.

All the crews then settled down for the night except those in *Weehawken* who were preparing an evil contraption invented by Ericsson. This was a 50ft raft for clearing mines and obstructions. It had a large notch into which the bows of the *Weehawken* fitted, to enable it to be pushed. Below the raft hung numerous 700lb charges set to explode on contact with anything. This fearsome device made the handling of the vessel very difficult, quite apart from the danger of it riding up over the bows, or even being caught under the overhang of the armour as the ship and raft pitched at different rates. Capt John

Rodgers feared a collision with a friendly ship and stated that 'He would be more dreaded than an enemy!'

THE ATTACK ON CHARLESTON

Dawn of the 6th broke to reveal dense fog, and although the ships crossed the bar the total lack of any visible landmarks made the trip up the narrow channel too hazardous to attempt. The attack was postponed until the following day.

By the morning of the 7th the fog had cleared, but due to adverse tidal conditions the force had to delay starting until 11.00am. *Weehawken*'s anchor got tangled up with the mine clearing raft and the whole force had to wait whilst it was sorted out. Cdr Rhind of the *Keokuk* decided this would be a good time to flood the ends of his vessel, but the pumps would not work. This was probably a good thing as it turned out!

Eventually, the squadron steamed up the channel towards Charleston led by *Weehawken*. The mine clearing raft had a serious effect on the control of this vessel and, as she meandered about the channel, the rest of the force had great difficulty in following in an orderly manner. They ended up all over the place and several near collisions occurred.

New Ironsides had the deepest draught of all the vessels and as she passed Fort Wagner, the leadsman called out the alarming news that there was barely a foot of water under the keel, so she anchored there and then. Also under the keel was a Confederate mine with electrical firing wires to the shore. However a farm cart had been driven over the wires on the beach and the mine would not work!

As the rest of the force approached the forts, they encountered numerous buoys which they suspected might have explosives attached. At about 2.50pm the first shot was fired at the lead ship *Weehawken* which soon became the target of fire from all directions. To make matters worse, an explosion occurred beneath the *Weehawken*'s bows, giving the vessel quite a shaking. This showed that there were indeed mines around and that Ericsson's ungainly raft was ineffective. *Weehawken* continued to lead the force until she came upon a line of obstructions right across the channel from Fort Sumter to Battery Bee (just NW of Fort Moultrie). Captain Rodgers quickly turned south to avoid running over them as he now had no faith in his raft. This sudden turn threw the rest of the squadron into confusion and the whole lot came to a near standstill under the combined fire of several forts to the north and west.

The attack on Charleston, 6 April 1863.

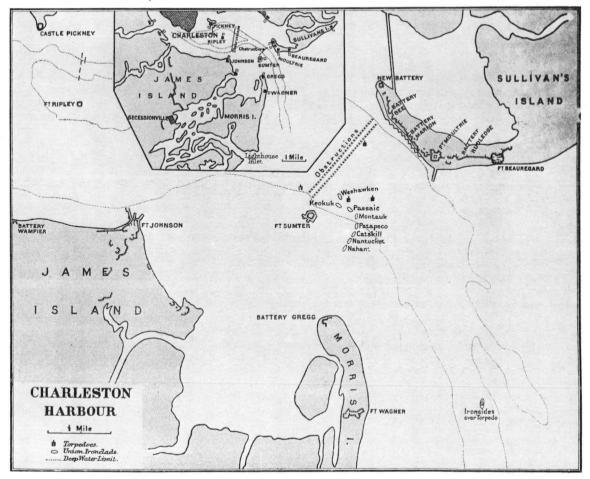

Close-up view of the lifeboat on the port side.

DAMAGE TO THE SQUADRON

The return fire from the ships was very slow, those with 15in guns taking up to 10 minutes to reload. These guns were expected to inflict heavy damage on the forts, but in the event they did no such thing. The main force came to within 1000yds of Fort Sumter. *Keokuk* got closest of all, reportedly within 300yds. She received all the attention one would expect at this distance, receiving 90 hits in 30 mins, 19 of these being on or below the waterline. Her experimental armour was poor and her gun-houses were riddled. The forts were wreaking havoc with all the vessels, *Weehawken* sustaining 50 hits in an hour. *Passaic*'s 15in gun was put out of action when its slide rails were bent. The vessel received 35 hits and the turret which also contained an 11in gun was jammed.

Montauk, a better protected ship sustained 14 hits without serious damage. During violent manoeuvring to avoid a collision, *Patapsco* lay nearly motionless for a few minutes between Forts Moultrie and Sumter, receiving their undivided attention. She stopped 47 shots in all, but suffered only a jammed turret.

This story was similarly repeated throughout the flotilla. *Nantucket* received 51 direct hits, several causing dents in the turret causing the gun port shutters to jam, while 36 hits on *Nahant* jammed her turret and damaged her steering gear.

In all, the attacking flotilla put up a rather poor show discharging a grand total of only 139 rounds. *Keokuk*

Keokuk viewed from astern.

Midships view showing base of funnel; note circular hatch abaft the funnel.

discharged only three rounds in all this time! The forts returned 2220 rounds, representing quite a good rate of fire. Good shooting it was too, representing a success rate of about 17%. Every ship suffered damage, *Keokuk* being by far the worse, her forward gun house was nearly demolished and she was taking water fast by the time she pulled out of action.

As *Keokuk* passed the *Ironsides*, Cdr Rhind signalled to DuPont that his ship was 'riddled like a colander'. Fortunately, her engines and boilers were undamaged and her pumps were just enough to keep her afloat. She limped away to the south of Morris Island, but the sea was rougher there and *Keokuk* sank in shallow water early the following morning. A tug accompanying the squadron stood by and took off all 92 crew of whom only 16 were wounded.

Keokuk's experimental lightweight armour, of which so much was expected, proved to be ineffective. Cdr Rhind felt that had the ship been built at the time she was designed she might have fared better. In a letter of 15 May 1863 he stated 'This vessel was offered to the Department early in 1861 and the contractors agreed to have her ready in 120 days, and if she had been built then she could have cleaned out every battery in the South, but it was not till after the success of the *Monitor* was made that her building was authorised and then the guns had got ahead of her.'

KEOKUK'S GUNS

Keokuk's story does not end there however. The fate of her guns provides an interesting insight into the shortages the Confederates were suffering.

Keokuk sank in about 18ft of water south of Morris Island within sight of Fort Sumter, about 4 miles away. Adm DuPont ordered the wreck to be destroyed and the long-suffering Rodgers of *Weehawken* was given the job. It was intended to push his raft of explosives, used in the battle, up to the wreck but rough seas and shallow water made this impractical and the attempt was abandoned. The Union force withdrew southwards, about 2 miles away.

Almost immediately the Confederates moved in and examined the sunken vessel. They decided to attempt to steal the two guns! The job was entrusted to one Adolphus La Costa, a civilian ordnance engineer, who had overseen the installation of the guns in the forts involved in the battle of only a few days previous. The job was a hard and dangerous one. Imagine having to cut tops out of two armoured gun-houses with saws, chisels and hammers, at night, within sight and gun-range of the Union force. The two guns, each 13½ft long and weighing about 8 tons had to be lifted out of the tops of the gun-houses and carried away. Then in the morning the wreck had to be left with no sign that it had been interferred with.

The forward gunhouse and funnel.

Two weeks of this work saw the gun-house tops cut away and the guns prepared for lifting. The guns had to be detached from their mounts below water-level before they could be lifted.

An old lightship hulk from Charleston was fitted with sheer-legs overhanging the bows by 20ft and around 1500 sandbags were also carried. The hulk was towed to the site at night by the steamer *Etivan*, their movements being concealed from the Union force by the dark background of Morris Island. The lightship hulk was manoeuvred to bring the sheer-legs over the gun and tackles were fixed. Finally, all the sandbags were brought up to the bows. The slack on the tackles was taken up and the gun lifted as far as possible by the men available. Further lifting was then achieved by moving all the sandbags from the bow to the stern. Sadly this was still not quite enough and just as the tired and disconsolate workers were about to give up, a strong swell lifted the gun clear! The coming of the dawn saw *Etivan* towing the hulk with its precious cargo past the Charleston forts, whose garrisons must have cheered loudly at the sight.

Three days later, on the 6 May, the second gun was successfully recovered. One gun went to Fort Sumter and the other to Battery Bee, the largest guns to be sited in these forts.

SUMMARY

Design submitted:	23 April 1861
Keel laid down:	19 April 1862
Launched:	6 December 1862
Commissioned	24 February 1863
Sunk	8 April 1863

Designed by Charles W Whitney
Built by J S Underhill, New York.
Commanding Officer: Cdr A C Rhind USN

Length:	159ft 6in
Beam:	36ft
Draught (mean)	8ft 6in
Displacement:	677 tons.

DOCUMENTS CONSULTED

1 *Specification of C W Whitney's Iron Mail Clad Floating Battery or Steam Gun Boat* Continental Iron Works, Green Point, Brooklyn. 23 April 1861.
2 Letter from C W Whitney to Rear Adm S F DuPont published in the *New York Times* on 24 April 1863.
3 Letter from Cdr A C Rhind USN to a Professor Soley and dated 15 May 1863.
4 *Plan of Engines for C W Whitney's Mail Clad Battery*
5 *Section of Armor proposed by C W Whitney*
All the above provided by Timothy K Nenninger, Navy & Old Army Branch, Military Archives Division, National Archives & Records Service, Washington DC 20408.
6 Embellished plan of USS *Keokuk* held by New York Historical Society. Facsimile supplied by: Capt JHB Smith USN, Head Curator Branch, Dept of the Navy, Naval Historical Center, Washington DC 20374
7 *Ironclads in Action* by H W Wilson (Sampson Low, London 1896)
8 *By Sea and by River: A Naval History of the Civil War* by Rear Adm B Anderson (1962)

LESSER KNOWN WARSHIPS OF THE KRIEGSMARINE

The Type 43 Minesweepers Part 2

by M J Whitley

The first ship to complete, *M601*, commissioned on 22 November 1944 but did not join the minesweeping flotillas, being used for development work with the new Construction Trials Command instead. It was not until the 1 December that the first operational flotilla was formed under the command of Kapitanleutnant Reinhart Ostertag. This was the re-formed 12th Flotilla whose previous ships had been lost in France. Three days later, in the forenoon of 3 December, Oberleutnant zur See d R Damerow commissioned his *M801* at Königsberg as the first ship of the flotilla. The designated leader, *M602* did not join the Fleet until noon on 14 December under Ob Ltn z See d R Kroeger but this unit had still not received her radar or *S Gerate* by the end of January 1945 although she was battle-worthy in all other respects.

By the end of January, the flotilla had eight ships: *M602* (Ob Kroeger), *M603* (Kp Lt D R Fremeroy), *M604* (Kpt Lt Anders), *M605* (Ob Lt d R Bellingrodt), *M801* (Ob Damerow), *M802* (Ob Lt d R Leimbach), *M803* (Kpt Lt d R Ahrens) and *M804* (Ob Lt Umbek). This was not its established full strength and the flotilla was attached to the 10th Security Division under the command of MOK (Ost).

The next eight units to complete were to be allocated to the 2nd Flotilla, reforming in Cuxhaven on 1 January 1945. However, of *M606 – M609* and *M805 – M808*, *M807* and *M808* remained incomplete at the end of the war and *M805* had been lost at the beginning of March.

Finally, the last flotilla to be projected was the 6th, scheduled to form on 15 March 1945, but none of its units (*M610, M809* to *M815*) were completed, with the exception of *M610* and that only under Allied supervision some five months after the close of hostilities.

The deteriorating situation on the Eastern Front led to the new ships being quickly deployed to assist in the massive rescue operations to evacuate East Prussia in the face of the Soviet advance. Barely commissioned, and lacking many items of equipment, *M801, M803* and *M804* were ordered by the OKM to break off work-up and minor repairs and to procede to Königsberg on 23 January 1945 to pick up refugees, where they joined the remainder of their class. Both flotillas remained fully occupied in the task of escorting refugee convoys until the final surrender. Soviet submarines were by now active in the southern Baltic and scored some success against the refugee convoy.

According to some sources, *M801* is credited with the sinking of the Soviet submarine *S4* by depth charges on 23 February but the war diary of Flag Officer (Destroyers) records that the torpedo boat *T3* (sic) rammed and sank a submarine in Danzig Bay on 4 January 1945, damaging her bows in the process and Jürg Meister in *Soviet Warships of the Second World War* (1977) gives the loss date of *S4* as 6 January 1945.

In May 1945, when the Allies entered the north German ports, they found the wrecks of *M802, M804* and *M805* on the bottom at Kiel, and *M804* broken in two at Monkeberg. The three wrecks came under category 'C' of the Tripartite Commission Report, ie those units captured non-operational, wrecked or incomplete and under the terms agreed were to be either destroyed for scrap or scuttled in no less than 100m of water by 15 August 1946. *M802* was partially demolished on 15 December 1945, then completely dispersed by two depth charges on 20 May 1946. *M805*'s wreck was destroyed on 17 August 1946.

POST WAR OPERATIONS

After the German surrender, most of the minesweepers, unlike other German warships, remained operational and were employed on clearing the vast wartime minefields around the continental coasts as part of the German Minesweeping Administration. *M601* to *M612* as well as *M806* took part in this operation. This organisation had been set up in accordance with Article

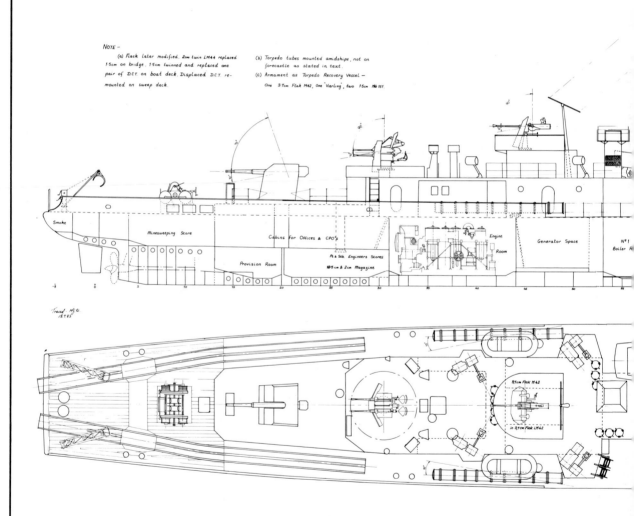

NOTE –

(a) Flack later modified. 2cm twin LM44 replaced 1.5cm on bridge. 1.5cm twinned and replaced one pair of D.C.T. on boat deck. Displaced D.C.T. re-mounted on sweep deck.

(b) Torpedo tubes mounted amidships, not on forecastle as stated in text.

(c) Armament as Torpedo Recovery Vessel – One 3.7cm Flak M42, One Vierling, two 1.5cm MG 151.

General arrangement of Type 43 Minesweeper

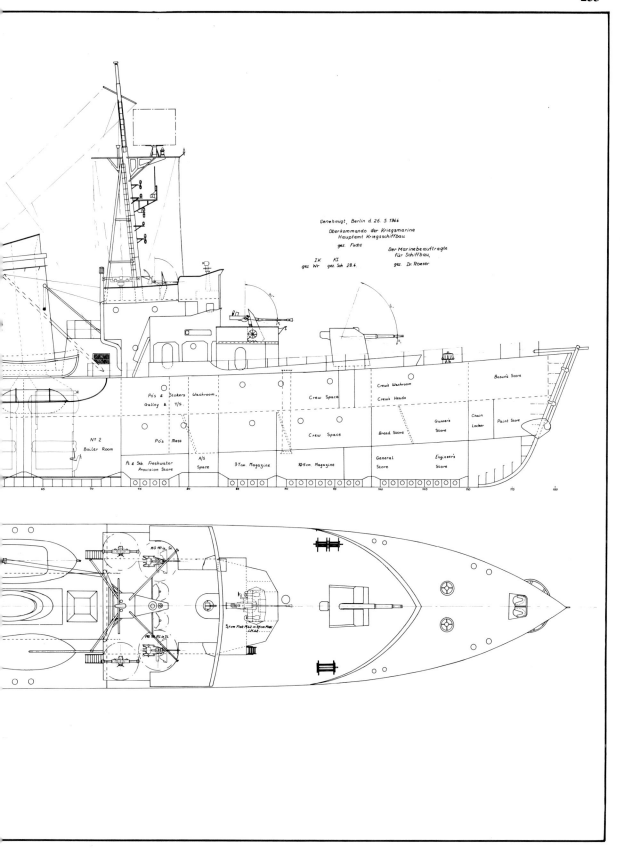

Genehmigt, Berlin d. 26. 5. 1944

Oberkommando der Kriegsmarine
Hauptamt Kriegsschiffbau

gez. Fuchs

IK   KI
gez. Wr   gez. Sch 28.4.

Der Marinebeauftragte
für Schiffbau,

gez. Dr. Roeser

Po's & Stokers Washroom.

Galley &   T/s

Crew Space

Crews Washroom

Crews Heads

Bosun's Store

Po's Mess

Crew Space

Bread Store

Gunner's
Store

Chain
Locker

Paint Store

N° 2
Boiler Room

Pt & Stb Freshwater
Provision Store

A/S
Space

3.7cm. Magazine

10.5cm. Magazine

General
Store

Engineer's
Store

MG 151 in SL.

MG in M.1 in SL.

3.7 cm Flak M.42 in 37cm Flak
L.M.42

7 of the Declaration regarding the defeat of Germany which was signed by the Allied C-in-Cs on 5 June 1945. It was divided into six divisions as follows:

1st Division, Schleswig-Holstein (Kiel)
2nd Division, Western Germany (Cuxhaven)
3rd Division, Denmark
4th Division, Norway
5th Division, Holland
6th Division, US Enclave (Bremen)

The ships were disarmed except for a maximum of two 2cm guns for mine sinking (except those employed in the Baltic where only ground mines were present). Their 10.5cm (4.1in) guns were, in most cases, retained but without breech blocks or ammunition. The personnel were drawn from serving former *Kriegsmarine* officers and men on a compulsory basis, (but no German occupied an operational position above flotilla commander). After the long years of hostilities there was, however, a natural desire by all former combatants to return home to civilian life and the Germans proved no exception. In consequence, desertion was a problem, which in turn caused manning difficulties. Morale was, in general, low, not surprisingly, since those formations stationed in former occupied territories were not allowed shore leave for obvious reasons. Furthermore, men having families in the Soviet Occupation zone or those coming out of those areas to Western areas were continually bombarded with Soviet propaganda extoling the delights of life in the Soviet zone. Under the conditions prevailing, this propaganda had some effect. Then in order to attract men to the service, advertisements were run in German newspapers. This however was frowned upon by the politicians and also attracted a vitriolic diatribe from the Soviets couched in the usual Marxist-Leninist terminology, accusing the Allies of seeking to maintain a disciplined, uniformed Fascist fleet! However, despite all these problems, the operation continued to function.

Its organisation was broadly based upon the flotilla dispositions as of the date of surrender, with some minor alterations. Flotillas were now known as 'German Minesweeper Flotillas' (GMSF). In August 1945, the organisation was as follows:

1st Division (Kiel)
2nd GMSF (*M606 – M611, M801, M371, M373, M374, M388*)
12th GMSF (*M601 – M605, M612, M806*)
23rd GMSF (8 'M40')
29th GMSF (10 'M40')
2nd Division (Cuxhaven)
1st GMSF (10 'M35,)
7th GMSF (7 'M35')
25th GMSF (9 'M40')
27th GMSF (9 'M40')
3rd Division (Denmark)
40th GMSF (3 'M35', 2 'M40', 9 'M16')
4th Division (Norway)
5th GMSF (8 'M35', Stavanger)
9th GMSF (5 'M40' Tromsö)
22nd GMSF (5 'M40', Bergen)
30th GMSF (7 'M40', Stavanger)

In addition, at Lorient, in France, the 24th GMSF had 3 'M40' ships, whilst in reserve or non-operational at St Nazaire, La Pallice and Lorient were a further 9 'M35', 10 'M40', and 1 'M43' (*M803* at La Pallice). Furthermore, there was a huge number of KFK flotillas also engaged on minesweeping.

Minesweeping operations were mainly conducted during the summer months, refits being undertaken during the winter when conditions were in general too rough for minesweeping. Strangely, in this period it was a shortage of coal which impeded, and on occasions halted, operations altogether, whereas oil had been the problem during the war, hence the coal-burning minesweepers (which comprised over 70% of the GMSF).

By 1946, the operation was being reduced as the surrendered warships due to Russia under the Tripartite Agreement began to be delivered. The 1st, 23rd, 29th and 30th Flotilla were handed over completely, with nine more ships from various other flotillas, but none of the modern Type 43 ships were obtained by the Soviets. However, it is believed that the incomplete hulls of *M807* and *M808* were later completed by the Soviet Navy and put into service. Their subsequent fate is not known, although they were probably discarded in the 1950s or 1960s. *M601* to *M605*, *M612* and *M806* were allocated to Britain, whilst *M606* to *M611*, *M801* and *M803* were allocated to the United States.

By 1947, the minesweeping task had been largely completed and the vessels concerned became surplus to requirements. Being coal burners, they were not in great demand for further service by any of the Allied Navies and most of the UK allocation began arriving in breakers yards during March and April 1948. Of the US vessels, three were sold out for commercial use in 1948 and three more sold to the Italian Navy in 1949. *M611*, one of the three sold out commercially in 1948 was later re-acquired by the USA and then on 15 August 1956, she was sold to the new German Navy with whom she remained in service as *Seeschlange* until paid off in February 1960 to become an accommodation ship. *M607* and *M608* still remain in commercial service under the Italian and Greek flags.

TABLE 3: CLASS LISTS

No	Launched	Commissioned	Fate
			Neptun Werft (Rostock) Vessels
M601	31.8.44	22.11.44	RN 1945. Arrived Middlesborough for scrapping 20.4.48
M602	21.10.44	14.12.44	RN 1945.
M603	2.11.44	31.12.44	RN 1945
M604	10.11.44	18.1.45	RN 1945. Arrived on Tyne for scrapping 28.3.48.
M605	13.12.44	3.2.45	RN 1945. Arrived on Thames for scrapping 17.3.48.
M606	20.12.45	20.2.45	USN 1945. B/U in Hamburg.
M607	20.12.44	16.3.45	USN 1945. Sold out commercially 1948*
M608	20.1.45	20.3.45	USN 1945. Sold out commercially 1948*
M609	29.1.45	27.3.45	RN 1945. Arrived Newcastle 17.2.48, B/U Dunstan.
M610	27.2.45	5.10.45	USN 1945. B/U Ghent 1950.
M611	12.3.45	12.3.45	USN 1945. Mercantile 1948, USN 1952, W Germany 1956.
M612	23.3.45	11.4.45	RN 1945, Arrived in Thames for B/U 17.3.48.
			Schichau (Königsberg) Vessels
M801	9.9.44	3.12.44	USN 1945. To Italy 20.7.49, *B3 – Gazella*. Discarded 1966.
M802	29.9.44	4.1.45	Sunk by 8th USAAF at Kiel 3.4.45.
M803	19.10.44	17.1.45	USN 1945. To Italy 20.7.49 *B2 – Daino*. Discarded 1966.
M804	1.11.44	23.1.45	Sunk by B24s of 8th USAAF at Kiel 11.3.45.
M805	9.11.44	26.1.45	Sunk by B24s of 8th USAAF at Kiel 11.3.45.
M806	21.11.44	1.45	RN 1945. Scrapped on Tyne 28.3.48.
M807	13.1.45		Completed by USSR.
M808	45		Completed by USSR.

Notes: *M613 – M616, M809 – M813* incomplete at surrender. Scrapped.
M601 – M604 ordered 7.5.43. Remainder 4.12.43.
*see below for commercial history.

COMMERCIAL HISTORIES

M607 Sold out 1948 to Hapag and renamed *Hornum*, then in 1950 sold again and renamed *Christian Ivers*, owners not known but managed by Ivers Linie of Kiel. 1953, sold to Kieler Reed Gmbh and in 1954 renamed *Hanne Scarlett*. Then in 1957 she was acquired by a trio of Danish businessmen, J O Jensen, L Jensen and J H J Jensen of Copenhagen but later that same year became owned solely by Jorgen Jensen. Four years later she was resold, this time to Skandinavisk Liniet-rafik AS also of Copenhagen. 1962 saw her renamed *Salvatore Lauro* on her sale to Agostino Lauro of Naples. Finally in 1975, Libera Navigazione Lauro S a S of Hong Kong became her owners, although still registered in Naples, with whom she is still in service.

M608 This ship had a similar career to that of *M607* until 1964, except that she was sucessively renamed *Arum*, *Harald Ivers* and *Lilli Scarlett*. In 1964, however, she was sold to Christos S Pagoulatos of Athens and renamed *Elena P*. She too, is still in service.

Both ships were re-engined with diesels early in commercial service.

TABLE 1: CLASS TECHNICAL DETAILS

Displacement:	605 tons (standard), 842 tons (full).
Length:	207ft (63.1m) pp, 224ft (68.3m) oa.
Beam:	29.5ft (9.0m).
Draught:	6.5/8.5ft (2.0/2.6m)
Machinery:	2 Wagner Marine Boilers (232 psi, 300° C); 2 sets triple expansion engines with Bauer-Wach exhaust turbines; 2400hp = 17kts maximum; 150 tons coal = 3600 miles at 10kts.
Armament:	2 – 10.5cm SKC/32ge (single mounts) – 210rpg HE, 30rpg star shell; 2 – 3.7cm Mk42 (single shielded mounts) – 1500rpg; 4 – 2cm C/38 (vierling) – 8000 rounds; 2 – 1.5cm Mg151 – 6000 rounds; some 2 – 53.3cm trainable MZ43 torpedo tubes; provision for 24 mines; 1 – 7.3cm 'Fohn' rocket launcher; (TRV's racks for 17 torpedoes in lieu of after 10.5).

TABLE 2: ARMAMENT

10.5cm SKC/30ns	(In 10.5cm centre pivot mounting MPLC/32ge)
Calibre	105mm (4.1in)
Muzzle Velocity:	780m/s (2559fps)
Shell weight:	15.1kg (33lb 4oz)
Shell length:	459mm (18in)
Filling weight:	3.8kg (12lb 7oz)
Complete round:	24kg (53lb)
Max Horiz Range:	15,175m (16,595yds, 8.2m)
Barrel length:	45 cal/474cm (15.5in)
Liner length:	42 cal/440cm (14.4in)
Constructional Gas Pressure:	2850kg/cm
Barrel life:	4100 rounds
Elevation/Depression:	70°/10°
Armour thickness:	12mm (front)4mm (side and deck)
Armour:	Wsh
Weight of barrel and breech:	1765kg (3891lb)
Weight of cradle and brakes:	655kg (1444lb)
Weight of mounting:	2100kg (4629lb)
Weight of shield:	1670kg (3681lb)
Weight of complete mount:	6750kg (14,880lb, 6.6 tons)
Rocket 'Fohn V2'	
Calibre:	7.3cm (2.8in)
Projectile weight:	2.64kg (5.8lb)
Propellant weight:	0.45kg (1lb)
Explosive charge:	0.3kg (10oz)
Range 0°:	300m (328yds)
Range 45°:	4200m (4593yds)
Range 90°:	2400m (2624yds)
Max trajectory vel:	280 – 300m/sec (918 – 984fs)
Fuze:	Proximity (time of flight 6.5sec) Percussion (RAZ 51)
Firing Rack weight:	600kg (1322lb)
No of launcher trays:	35 (7 horizontal in 5 tiers)
Target area at 1400/1600m:	35 rockets HE in 90m × 120m (98 × 131yds). Fired as one salvo or two halves. Rockets in magazine clips of 7.

Actual warfare concentrates wonderfully the minds of naval aircraft designers, but it also has the effect of sorting the wheat from the chaff, and in our column for this issue we are taking a brief look at an aircraft that was conceived to meet a pressing demand from the Fleet Air Arm but which, for a variety of reasons, was to play no part in the conflict which spawned it.

The wheat in this instance was the Supermarine Seafire, a by and large successful adaptation of the remarkable Spitfire landplane and to which we might return in a future column; the chaff with which we are here concerned was an aircraft expressly designed to fill the role that the Seafire would assume – a single-seat fleet air defence fighter, successor to the Blackburn Skua (but closer in concept to the Sea Gladiator and, as it transpired, the stopgap Fulmar and Martlet) and called Firebrand.

Designed to Specification N11/40 and first flown in February 1942, the new aircraft could hardly have presented a greater contrast in appearance to the machines it was supposed to replace. It was, by the FAA standards of the day, a massive aeroplane: not only did its airframe exceed the dimensions of existing carrier-based fighters, it was also half as heavy again as the RN's Albacore torpedo-bomber; indeed, it surpassed in size the Grumman Tarpon (Avenger) torpedo-bomber then evincing quizzical Admiralty glances from across the Atlantic.

In retrospect, it is not easy to determine just why the Firebrand should have emerged as the bulky aircraft it did; certainly the Napier Sabre powerplant was a hefty piece of machinery, but on the other hand the RAF's Typhoon, which also used the Sabre (and, incidentally, a naval version of which was the Firebrand's defeated competitor for N11/40), weighed only some four tons (empty) as compared with the Blackburn aircraft's five. Additionally, carrier requirements such as wing folding, undercarriage, strengthening and flap mechanisms would account for extra weight, but in general the design seems to have had far less compromise than naval aircraft design in reality demanded.

In fact, both the Sabre engine and the bulk of the aircraft itself, together with the proof that the Seafire was indeed a viable carrier fighter, were the major contributors to the abandonment of development of the Firebrand as a fighter: the Typhoon was accorded top priority for development as the RAF's ground attack fighter and hence Sabre production was concentrated for that purpose; meanwhile the Firebrand's deck-

Warship Wings No 7

Blackburn Firebrand

By Roger Chesneau

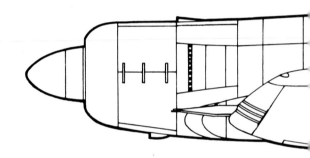

landing characteristics were proving to be something less than ideal.

However, re-engined, the enormous airframe might be put to better use, and with Admiralty encouragement Blackburn started work to reconfigure the project as a torpedo aircraft, retaining the wing-mounted cannon to give the Firebrand a fighter capability as well, something of a change for the FAA since the single seat was to be central to the design. One of the prototypes was rebuilt to undertake trials as such (Firebrand Mk II) and further Mk Is were married to the powerful Bristol Centaurus radial (Firebrand Mk III). The Mk III flew at the end of 1943, but although, somewhat ironically, the re-engined torpedo-fighter variant proved handier and more manoeuvrable in the air than the Mk I fleet air defence fighter, there were still problems in carrier handling, notably approach. The Firebrand was relatively docile at low speeds to be sure, but the view forward, of especial importance to an aircraft whose wingspan amounted to two-thirds the width of a typical flight deck, was virtually non-existent: pilots were reportedly unable to see *any part* of the flight deck during the last few dozen yards of their approach path. How the Firebrand would have faired landing aboard

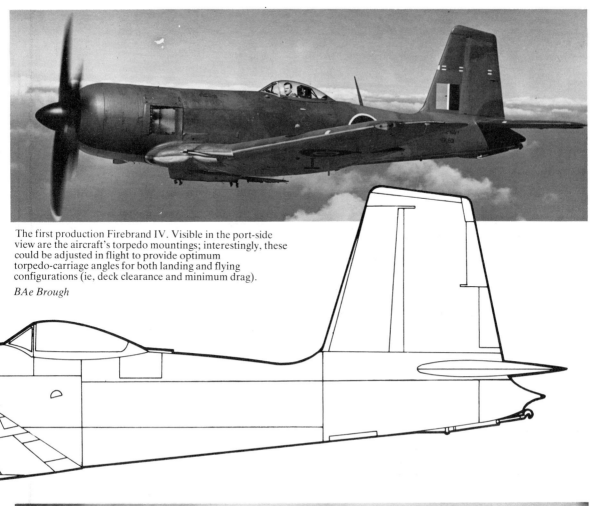

The first production Firebrand IV. Visible in the port-side view are the aircraft's torpedo mountings; interestingly, these could be adjusted in flight to provide optimum torpedo-carriage angles for both landing and flying configurations (ie, deck clearance and minimum drag).

BAe Brough

A Firebrand Mk V rolls aboard *Implacable*. Note the large Fowler-type flaps and the stabilising fins fitted to the torpedo slung below the fuselage. Note also the zero-length rocket rails below the wings: the Firebrand could also operate in the conventional strike role.

Fleet Air Arm Museum

1

3

2

1 The second prototype Firebrand III. The rudder is considerably larger than that first fitted, to counter the torque produced by the propeller.

BAe Brough

2 A production Firebrand IV. The photo gives some indication of the appalling view forward offered to the pilot.

BAe Brough

3 Another Firebrand IV in early postwar colour scheme. The small fairings before the cockpit housed an airspeed indicator, for use by pilots during landing.

BAe Brough

carriers like *Argus* or *Furious*, with no, or at best vestigial, islands, can perhaps be imagined.

As events turned out, the Blackburn torpedo-fighter had no such opportunity, since it was September 1945 before the Mk IV – the production variant and the subject of further design changes – was brought into service. Further small modifications produced the Mks V and VA, and the aircraft went to sea aboard *Illustrious* and *Implacable* during the late 1940s; it also formed part of the initial equipment of the new carrier *Eagle* from March 1952, but within a year or so had been withdrawn in favour of the Westland Wyvern.

BLACKBURN FIREBRAND MK IV – SPECIFICATION

Overall length:	38ft 9in
Span:	51ft 3in (full); 16ft 1in (folded)
Max height:	13ft 3in
Wing area:	383ft²
Engine:	1 – Bristol Centaurus IX piston engine, 2520hp
Max speed:	300kts at 13,000ft
Combat radius:	320nm
Weight:	11,500lb (5.1 tons) empty; 16,700lb (7.4 tons) max
Weapons:	4–20mm Hispano cannon, 1–18in Mk XV/XVII torpedo

THE FINAL ACTION

The Sinking of Bismarck, 27 May 1941

By John Roberts

On the morning of 27 May 1941 the German battleship *Bismarck* was steaming an erratic north westerly course well out in the Atlantic, west of the English Channel. Six days earlier she had sailed from Bergen to raid the

Atlantic convoy routes, a move frustrated by her action of 24 May which, although resulting in the sinking of battlecruiser *Hood*, required an early return to port to repair damage inflicted by the battleship *Prince of Wales*. By circuitous route she headed for Brest but on 26 May Swordfish aircraft from *Ark Royal* hit her with two torpedoes one of which jammed her rudder 20° to

Bismarck as completed.
IWM, courtesy R A Burt

port and damaged her propellers. Attempts to release the rudder failed and steering using only the engines achieved only minimal success. Alone and crippled she could only await the arrival of her pursuers. Away to the north the battleships *King George V*, flying the flag of Admiral Sir John Tovey C-in-C Home Fleet, and *Rodney* approached at a moderate speed with the intention of bringing *Bismarck* to action at dawn.

THE GUN DUEL

As dawn neared *King George V* and *Rodney* began to work up speed as they approached the *Bismarck*'s reported position from the WNW. A Force 6 gale was blowing from the NW generating a heavy swell but dawn showed a clear, overcast day with good visibility. At 0820 the masts of the cruiser *Norfolk* came into view and this ship, which had been shadowing *Bismarck* since 0753, reported the enemy's exact position.

The two British battleships were steering 110° with *Rodney* 1600yds off the flagship's port quarter when, at 0842, *Bismarck* was sighted from *King George V* bearing green (starboard) 7°. One minute later the Air Defence Officer aboard *Rodney* also sighted the German battleship, 25,000yds away (12.3nm), steering directly towards the British ships and listing 3° to 5° to port. For both British ships range-taking conditions were poor, due to the long range and funnel haze, and fire control tables were initially set to estimated ranges (25,000yds in *Rodney* and 24,000yds in *King George V*). However, the flagship's Type 284 gunnery radar obtained a momentary echo at 25,100yds and her table was returned to this range; the Type 284 continued to

Rodney in August 1941.
Perkins, courtesy R A Burt

obtain short echoes until the range dropped below 21,100yds (10.4nm) when they became continuous.

At 0847 *Rodney* opened fire with A and B turrets at a gun range of 23,500yds, followed by *King George V* one minute later at 24,600yds. *Bismarck* replied at 0849, firing on *Rodney* with her forward turrets; her first 4-gun salvo fell 1000yds short; the second 1000yds over; the third (at 0853) straddled, one shell falling only 20yds short just abaft the bridge but causing no casualties and the rest over; the next two salvos fell short, after which there were several overs. Although *Bismarck*'s initial fire was good it was not as accurate as expected and it seems likely she was suffering similar difficulties of observation as the British, combined with her problems of maintaining a steady course. She never did find her target and very soon after the action began damage greatly reduced her fire control capability and armament. Nevertheless, on several occasions her fall of shot came uncomfortably close to the British ships.

Rodney found her target with her second double, fired 0848 (unfortunately not spotted by *Rodney*), *Norfolk* reporting that hits were obtained with one or both of these salvos. At 0850 *Rodney*'s main director rangefinder obtained a plot 2500yds above gun range and, as no range had as yet been obtained from spotting

the fall of shot, her fire control table was tuned to this range. Consequently, *Rodney* was firing 'over' for several minutes and did not regain her target until salvo 18, the 'B' of a down ladder, at about 0859 at a range of 21,000yds. This straddle was seen to produce two hits on *Bismarck*, one on the forecastle and another which sent a sheet of flame up the superstructure. It is probable that this hit on the forecastle put *Bismarck*'s turret out of action. *Rodney* continued to straddle her target until 0902 obtaining several hits.

At 0853 *King George V* signalled for the ships to turn 085° together but *Rodney* was already committed to a port turn to open her 'A' arcs and for a short period the British ships were steaming on diverging courses. At 0853 *Rodney* turned to starboard onto an easterly course, closing the 'A' arcs after 'X' turret had fired in only two salvos (X turret was able to fire in three more salvos 17, 18 and 19 when a small alteration of course was made to avoid enemy fall of shot).

The fall of shot of *King George V*'s first salvo was not seen but the Type 284 reported this as short so an up ladder was fired. However, it was later concluded that the 284 had ranged on *Rodney*'s shell splashes and consequently for a few minutes *King George V*'s salvos fell over. At 0853 the Type 284 obtained a range of 20,500yds and a double, spread 200yds on each side of this (ie 20,300yds and 20,700yds), was fired. The 'A' salvo straddled and produced the first hit actually observed by the flagship. After this *King George V* fired zig-zag salvos using the ranges obtained on the

Type 284 – observing the fall of shot revealed that a correction of 200yds down was required on the radar range, which was in-line with earlier experience in practice firing. Until 0913, when the Type 284 broke down as a result of a heavy shaking from 14in gun blast, at a range of 12,400yds, 14 straddles was observed out of about 34 salvos. Even allowing for spotting errors this was exceptionally good both in terms of fire control and rate of fire – a few salvos fell out of line (ie off the bearing) but the target was only lost twice (on both occasions a regaining ladder was fired) – some salvos were not observed due to cordite smoke.

At 0854 *Norfolk* to the north of *Bismarck* opened fire with her 8in guns and four minutes later *Rodney*'s starboard 6in battery joined in at a range of 21,000yds. By 0900 the fire from *Bismarck* had slackened; 'A' turret was probably out of action, B was firing spasmodically and the after turrets were still unable to bear on the British ships. At 0902 *Bismark*'s foretop fire control post was put out of action and shortly afterwards the lower fire control position on the conning tower, together with both forward turrets, were also put out of action. At 0908 *Norfolk* reported that the guns of 'A' turret were laying depressed as if the elevating gear had gone, while those of 'B' were pointing drunkenly towards the sky. It has been recorded that A or B turret fired a last salvo at 0927 – it is possible that one or more guns were able to fire, perhaps on a fixed bearing, due to the efforts of the turret crews on the other hand it may just be an error of observation.

Just after 0902 *King George V* and *Rodney* turned onto a course of 182°, with *Rodney* well aft, just off the flagship's port quarter. The action was still only 15 minutes old. This southerly course proved difficult for gun control in *Rodney* as the heavy swell on the starboard quarter made the ship yaw badly, and cordite and funnel smoke made ranging difficult. *King George V* employing radar control was much less affected by these conditions although she still, of course, had spotting difficulties. At 0909 *Rodney* altered course 40° to port placing the wind dead astern which improved conditions slightly.

At 0910 *Bismarck*'s after turrets, controlled from the after control post, began firing at *King George V* but three minutes later, after firing only four salvos which were getting progressively closer to their target the director was disabled. Control was transferred to the turrets themselves which continued to fire independently until D turret was put out of action at 0921 (the right gun was wrecked by a premature detonation, two more rounds were fired from the left gun before internal damage brought firing to a stop) and C turret ceased fire at 0931 after the left gun was disabled by a hit. (*Bismarck* had shifted her fire back to *Rodney* at 0920.) Thus, 45 minutes from the start of the action, all of *Bismarck*'s main armament and fire control gear was out of action.

At 0915 *Bismarck* began to draw aft from the British ships and both turned 180° (*Rodney* to starboard and *King George V* to port) bringing them onto a similar course to the enemy. As *King George V* turned A and B

turrets continued to fire while Y turret trained round to pick up the target again at 12,000yds as the A arcs opened on the opposite beam. *Rodney* turned at 0916 after firing her 40th salvo, which straddled, and both main and secondary armament had to check fire while she turned, fire being re-opened by the main armament at 10,000yds at 0918 and shortly afterwards by the starboard 6in battery. Both ships had difficulty spotting on this northerly course because the *Bismarck* was continuously surrounded by shell splashes and the after part of the ship was shrouded in smoke from fires and her funnel. Without radar *King George V*'s performance was reduced but four straddles were spotted between 0913 and 0930 and on three occasions she regained the target by firing a single ladder and once with two ladders. In addition at 0920 she began to experience trouble with breakdowns in her 14in mountings, which so reduced the numbers of guns able to fire that all those still operating were fired together to provide adequate salvos. At 0929 she started using her Type 279 radar to range on *Bismarck* and reverted to firing zig-zag salvos until 0953 when the radar was transferred to its usual function of air search. During this time the *King George V* continually bracketted her target with the 'A' salvos over and the 'B' salvos under but only three straddles and one hit were observed.

Rodney fared much better, with the wind on the port bow-spotting and range taking conditions improved but the swell produced a heavy roll. On her new course she regained the target with three down ladders, obtaining a straddle with the 'A' salvo of the 3rd ladder at 9000yds at 0920. She continued to straddle *Bismarck* for the next eight minutes, only one regaining ladder being necessary. At 0921 she altered course to 021° and at 0926 to 037° which increased the roll and made range taking difficult (no ranges were obtained between 0922 and 0927). At 0928 the target was lost and until 0945 great difficulty was experienced in regaining and holding the target. Hits were obtained at 0929 and 0935 but all other salvos (when observed) were reported 'over' or 'short', due to an error in the TS (Transmitting Station) as well as the difficulties already mentioned.

Rodney's course gradually took her across *Bismarck*'s bows and at 0936 she turned 180° to port and began a pattern of crossing back and forth raking the enemy ship from ahead at range between 4000 and 3000yds. She turned again at 0942. No straddles were obtained on the first leg of this zig-zag course but when fire was reopened at 0945 the fourth salvo obtained hits. Thereafter she continuously hit and straddled the target until cease fire at 1014.

At 0949 she again turned 180° but shortly afterwards the AFCT broke down and fire had to continue under the direct control of the director until, having found the damage to the table could not be repaired, control was rerouted through one of the Vickers AFCC (used normally for the secondary armament). At 0952 full broadsides were ordered, the first was short but the remainder scored hits, as many as five or six being observed in one broadside. At 1003, having altered

King George V on 10 July 1942.
NMM

Bismarck in the Atlantic, May 1941.
IWM, courtesy R A Burt

course 190° to starboard she fired her last broadside at 4000yds and then reverted to salvo firing to avoid waste of ammunition. At 1005 she again altered course as the guns were bearing aft and in her last twelve salvos, between 1008 and 1014 at an average 3800yds range scored several hits. She then turned north to rejoin the *King George V*.

Meanwhile between 0954 and 1009 *King George V* obtained at least three straddles while her zig-zag salvos generally bracketed the target at an average range of 8000yds. From 0955 to 1004 control was transferred to the after DCT while the flagship turned 180° to starboard but 5 minutes later fire had to be checked when she again turned 180° to close the range to 4000yds before opening fire again at 1018. At 1019 a 3-gun salvo was seen to obtain three hits one of which, on B turret, started a fire and caused the back of the turret to be blown out, while the other two hit the base of the forward superstructure and started a large fire which sent flames as far up as the bridge platform – at the time *Bismarck* was head on to *King George V*.

King George V ceased fire at 1021 and, as both British battleships were short of fuel, she joined *Rodney* and steered 027° at 19kts for home. *Bismarck* was a complete wreck, very low in the water and on fire but her flag still flew and she showed no immediate signs of sinking. Admiral Tovey ordered any ships in the area that still had torpedoes to close and sink her. At 1025 the cruiser *Dorsetshire* fired two torpedoes into her starboard side which appeared to have no immediate effect so she steamed around to the other side and fired a third torpedo. Four minutes later *Bismarck* capsized, she sank shortly after in position 48°10′N, 16°12′W.

FIRE CONTROL

In the early stages of the action, until 0913, *King George V* employing her Type 284 radar had an advantage over *Rodney* and obtaining about 14 straddles to *Rodney*'s 8 or 9. It is difficult however, to attribute any particular damage to either ship – it was during this period that *Bismarck*'s A and B turrets and the forward fire control positions were disabled. After 0913 *King George V*'s fire was considerably reduced, initially by the loss of her Type 284 and subsequently by problems with her 14in mountings, and it seems likely that most of the damage done to *Bismarck*, including the disabling of the after control post and turrets, in the period 0915 until 0930 was inflicted by *Rodney*. As the range closed both ships again began to hit consistently, *Rodney* from about 0945 and *King George V* from about 0953.

Spotting for both ships was very difficult due to smoke interference, the heavy swell, *Bismarck*'s continual yaw due to her damaged rudder and the difficulties of distinguishing between the 14in and 16in fall short of shot (further confused by the shell splashes of the secondary armament and the 8in fire of the cruisers *Norfolk* and *Dorsetshire*).

16in GUN MOUNTING PERFORMANCE

Under the circumstances *Rodney*'s 16in Mk I triples performed exceptionally well and there can be little doubt that she did a great deal of damage to *Bismarck*. Her mountings had once given a great deal of trouble and the relative smoothness with which they operated on 27 May 1941 seemed to prove that during her 15 years of service most of the problems had been ironed out. Her performance was all the more creditable when considering that she had only carried out one live firing practice since the previous year and no night firing practice since the outbreak of war. In addition, a week before the action 30 men, mostly leading seamen and petty officers, had left the ship (as she was about to leave for the USA for refit these key personnel could be found more important duties!) resulting in a dilution of the personnel and in particular a reduction in the efficiency of the guns crews.

Nevertheless, the output of her main armament for the first 30 minutes was 90%, at one time firing 3 salvos per minute. In the first hour she achieved 80% with 1.5 salvos per minute. Overall she produced 1.6 salvos per minute during salvo firing and 1.1 broadsides per minute during broadside firing, with outputs of 77% and 62% respectively.

She experienced various minor problems with mechanical failures and drill errors, the worst being with the right gun of A turret. This gun missed 11 salvos due to problems with the slide locking gear and then, at salvo 65, a complete jam occurred in the right shell pusher hoist. As a result of drill errors the top shell was rammed up the hoist and jammed in the gunhouse with its nose against the rangefinder supports. It was not cleared until 12 hours after the action. In addition the centre gun of A missed 2 salvos due to slow drill and all the salvos from 64 to 88 due to mechanical failures, the left gun of A missed 10 salvos and did not fire after salvo 97 due to mechanical failures. B turret's centre gun misfired at salvo 4 and missed 5 or 6 over a period of 7 minutes towards the end of the action due to drill errors. The left gun of B had several delays as a result of drill errors but X turret suffered only two jams which caused only minor delays.

14in GUN MOUNTING PERFORMANCE

King George V's problems were much worse, largely due to the fact that the 14in twin and quadruple mountings were comparatively new and were suffering a considerable number of teething problems. Initially she did well achieving 1.7 salvoes per minute while employing radar control but she began to suffer severe problems from 0920 onward. 'A' turret was completely out of action for 30 minutes, after firing about 23 rounds per gun, due to a jam between the fixed and revolving structure in the shell room and Y turret was out of action for 7 minutes due to drill errors. The left gun of B had several delays as a result of drill errors but X turret suffered only two jams which caused only minor delays. Both guns in B turret, guns 2 and 4 in A turret and gun 2 in Y turret were put out of action by jams and remained so until after the action – 5 guns out of 10! There were a multitude of other problems with mechanical failures and drill errors that caused delays and missed salvoes. There were also some missfires – one gun (3 of A turret) misfired twice and was out of action for 30 minutes before it was considered safe to open the breech.

DAMAGE TO RODNEY

Little of the damage received by *Rodney* was inflicted by *Bismarck*. She did not receive a direct hit but did have slight splinter damage from near misses. Three minor holes were made in the bridge structure one of which cut the control leads to the searchlights. The base of a 5.9in shell penetrated the side of the CPOs' mess and caused some slight damage and another fragment penetrated the side of the HA director and ricocheted about inside. In addition a considerable number of electricity cables were cut and the sluice valve door of the starboard torpedo tube was jammed.

This damage, however, paled into significance compared with the havoc wrought by the blast of her own main armament. The upper deck was depressed to varying depths around the turrets and partition bulkheads, beams and support pillars had been distorted and split between the upper and main decks. Ventilation trunks had been split and blown out. The wooden deck planking had been ripped up and in some places sections were missing, many of the deck fittings had been broken and distorted. The watertight hatch over the sick bay was blown open and the area below completely wrecked.

In the *Rodney*'s torpedo flat the entire complement of torpedoes were fired without success but not without

considerable difficulty. Vibration from the main armament and near misses started the rivets in the fresh tanks immediately over the torpedo body room and water began to seep down into the flat. In addition all the lamps were shattered and light had to be provided by portable lamps and torches. When the starboard sluice valve door jammed it was twice opened with difficulty but after that seized up solid and all torpedoes had to be fired from the port tube. With only two torpedoes left the deck head began to sag, the depression of the deck forward caused by the gun blast having transmitted itself to the lower and the beam on which the torpedo traversing trolley ran dropped 1in. Both the remaining torpedoes were on the starboard side and to fire them it was necessary to transfer them to the port tube with this traversing trolley. The torpedoes, however, would not clear the loading rack and it was necessary to bump them over.

DAMAGE TO BISMARCK

The full effect of the British shellfire on the *Bismarck* is, apart from the damage to the armament and upperworks, difficult to evaluate. Two points of controversy have clouded this issue, the statements by survivors that the main belt was not pierced and that scuttling charges were used to sink her. However, there were no survivors from the fore end of the ship, so such statements can only be accepted with certainty as applying to the after part of the ship. No evidence exists, to prove or disprove that *Bismarck* was penetrated below the armoured main deck but the two decks above it, both from the evidence of survivors and observation by British ships were subject to considerable damage. This at the very least required the penetration of either the 50mm (2in) upper deck – at long range – or the 145mm (5.6in) upper belt. However, the most direct evidence

Bismarck early in May 1941, viewed from *Prinz Eugen.*
Drüppel, courtesy R A Burt

of armour penetration comes from *King George V* which obtained one or possibly two hits on *Bismarck*'s B turret at a range of 4000yds. These appeared to go through the armour and blow out the back of the turret throwing part of the armour plate over the side. These shells were fired from nearly right ahead, so probably went through the turret's side which was 220mm (9in forward and 150mm (6in) rear thick, unless the turret was trained ahead (the face plates were 380mm – 15in thick). At such short range they certainly would not have penetrated the sloping roof plates. Some deliberate waterline shots were fired by both *Rodney* and *King George V* at close range in the latter part of the action but *Bismarck* was low in the water and listing to port (the engaged side) so much if not all of the thickest belt armour was probably submerged.

Damage to the upperworks and higher decks was considerable and severely disrupted the communication systems (which were mainly above the main armoured deck). Some British shells passed through the ship and exploded on the starboard (disengaged side) while others, hitting the superstructure, passed right through without exploding (a 1in mild steel plate, hit at the normal was required to initiate the 159 fuze fitted to 16in and 14in APC). *Rodney* estimated that she obtained 40 16in hits, those achieved by *King George V* are not known but one would assume a similar number. Although these would seem sufficient to cause the *Bismarck* to sink, the majority would have caused damage above water, particularly those fired at close range (from which the majority of hits were obtained) and, as it is necessary to admit water to a ship to sink her, it is not perhaps surprising that she appeared to be foundering very slowly.

Survivors state that orders were given to scuttle the ship just after 1000, however, this does not indicate a well organised system of laying scuttling charges around the ship. First, only those stations still in communication with whoever gave the order would have been able to carry out that order, and communications had been severely disrupted; second, the scuttling order related more to the opening of seacocks, valves, watertight doors and so on than the blowing holes in the bottom of the ship (survivors have said they saw not evidence of damage to the ship's hull when she capsized). Two of the ship's three engine rooms and the after damage control post received the order to scuttle (and possibly others) in each case steps were taken to flood the compartments concerned the only charges mentioned being those fitted to the sea intakes of the condensers in the engine room. The only clue that these steps had an effect is in the fact that she sank stern first when most of the shellfire damage was forward. On the other hand it is hardly fair to assume that the gunfire and *Dorsetshire*'s torpedoes had a minimal effect on the speed with which she sank particularly as she capsized to port – the engaged side – which survivors could not have seen. Personally I am of the opinion that *Bismarck* would have sunk and that any scuttling measures were only partial and served only to hasten that end.

TABLE 1: HMS RODNEY RECORD OF 16in SALVOS

Time	Salvo	Correction	Range (yds)	Fall of Shot	Notes
0847	1A	Spread for	23,500	R	
	2B	deflection		L & R	
0848	3A	Spread for		None in	Hits observed
	4B	deflection		line	from *Norfolk* from 3 or 4 or both
0850	5A	Spread for		R	
	6B	deflection at new range		R	
0851	7A	L1		Over	
	8B	L2		Over	
0852	9A	Down ladder		L	
	10B			L	
0854	11A	R		Over	
	12B	R		Over	
0855	13A	Down ladder		L	
	14B			L	
0856	15A	R4		Over	
0856	16B	R2		Over	
0858	17A	Down ladder	21,000	Over	
	18B			Straddle	
0900	19A	Zig-zag		Straddle	
	20B	group		Straddle	
0901	21A	None		Straddle	
	22B	None		Over	
0902	23A	Down ladder		Over	
	24B			Straddle	
0904	25	None		Over	
	26	D400		Over & L	
0905	27	D400, R2		Straddle	
	28	None		Not clearly seen	
	29	D400		?	
0905	30	U400		R	
0908	31A	L2		Not clearly	One of 31 or 32
	32B	L1		seen	obtained hits
0911	33A	Zig-zag		Not seen	
	34B	group		Not seen	
	35A	None		Short	
	36B	U400		Over	
0914	37A	D200		Over	
	38B	D400		Over	Correction error
0915	39A	Down ladder		Over	
0916	40B			Straddle	
0918	41A	New course	10,000	Over	
	42B	(spread for line)		Over	
	43A	Down ladder		Over	
	44B			Over	
0920	45A	Down ladder	9000	Straddle	
	46B			Short	
0922	47A	Zig-zag		Straddle	
	48B	group		Straddle	
	49A	Zig-zag		Over	
	50B	group		Over	
	51A	Down ladder		Over	
	52B			Straddle	
	53A	None		Straddle	
	54B	None		Straddle	
	55A	Zig-zag		Straddle	
	56B	group		Straddle	
	57A	None		Straddle	
	58B	None		Straddle	
0928	59A	1st salvo of zig-zag		Short	

	60	U400	Over
0929	61A	D200	Short
	62B	Zig-zag group	Short
	63A	U400	Straddle	Hits observed
	64B	U400	Mostly over
	65	D200	Over
	66A	D400	Over
	67B	D400	Over
0932	68A	D800	Short	Correction error
	69B	U400	
Over	70A	D200	Short
	71B	U400	Over
	72A	D400	Short
	73B	U200	Straddle	Hits observed
	74	None	Straddle	Hits observed
	75	None	Straddle	Hits observed
0938	76	Fired on mean of RF ranges	Over
	77	Fired on mean of RF ranges	Over
	78A	Down ladder	Short
	79B		Short
	80	U800	Over
	81	D400	Over
	82A	Down ladder	Short
	83B		Short
	84		Over
0945	85		Short
	86	U400	Over
	87	D400	Over
0945	88-89		Straddle	Hits observed
	90-92		?	AFCT broke down
0952	93	Broadside	Short
	94	U400, broadside		Hits observed
	95-97	None, broadsides		Hits observed
	98	D200, broadside		Attempt at hits on waterline
1003	99	Last broadside	4000
	100-101	Salvos	
1008-1014	102-113	Salvos	3800 (mean)	Several hits obtained

Notes: L = left; R = right; corrections for bearing (ie L1, L2 is left one unit, left 2 units). U = up; D = down; corrections for range (ie U400 = up 400yds, D200 = down 200yds); A and B indicate 'A' and 'B' salvos of ladders or zig-zag groups; ladders, fired up or down, consisted on two salvos fired in succession without waiting to spot the fall of the first salvo (ie if a fall of shot was spotted over, a down ladder would be fired the 'A' salvo being 400yds down on the previous salvo, and the 'B' salvo a further 400yds down on that – 200yd and 800yd steps were also used depending on circumstances), the next correction would be based on the spotting of both salvos. When the target was found a zig-zag group was fired to give a spread of shells over the target's position.

TABLE 2: 16in AMMUNITION EXPENDITURE IN RODNEY

Turret	Gun	Rounds fired
A	L	36
A	C	46
A	R	22
B	L	45
B	C	44
B	R	52
X	L	44
X	C	42
X	R	44
	TOTAL	375

TABLE 3: 14in AMMUNITION EXPENDITURE IN KING GEORGE V

Turret	Gun	Rounds fired
A	1	22
A	2	27
A	3	30
A	4	32
B	1	36
B	2	40
Y	1	21
Y	2	45
Y	3	37
Y	4	49
	TOTAL	339

TABLE 4: BRITISH AMMUNITION EXPENDITURE

Ship	Gun Calibre	Ammunition	Rounds Fired
King Geogre V	14in	APC Mk VIIB	339
King George V	5.25in	SAP MkIC (Fuze 501)	660
Rodney	16in	APC MkIB (Fuze 159)	375
Rodney	6in	CPBC Mk XXVB (Fuze 480)	716
Norfolk	8in	–	527
Dorsetshire	8in	–	254

Notes: Rodney fired 150 salvos from her starboard 6in battery (5 salvos/min) and 98 salvos from her port 6in battery (3.9 salvos/min). During the first 9 minutes at close range the 6in achieved 5.9 rounds per minute and an output of nearly 100%. In King George V the starboard 5.25in battery fired approximately 70 rounds per gun (except S4 left gun which misfired after 12 rounds) and the port battery about 29 rounds per gun.

THE MAJESTIC PRE DREADNOUGHT Part 2 by R A Burt

Launch of the *Prince George* on 22 August 1895. The photograph shows clearly the recess for the 9in belt, which covered 220ft of the ship's side.

IWM

The armour layout of the *Majestic* was designed to give maximum protection against the ever developing threat of attack from medium calibre guns and HE shells, the main belt was reduced in thickness to increase its area and give improved protection to the middle side, above which the majority of hits were expected in any action. The principal improvements in armour layout were:

1 General use of Harvey armour for the vertical main belts, in place of Nickel or Compound armour or plain steel.

2 Adoption of a much wider belt, made possible by the reduction of thickness over previous classes, backed by a sloping deck (instead of a flat deck placed on top of the main armour strake as before). Again this helped in reducing thickness without excessive loss of protection.

3 Provision of closed armoured shields (turrets) over the barbettes which afforded much protection for the guns and guns crews.

The sloping deck employed in the Royal Navy for many years and extensively copied abroad, originated in a desire to provide deck protected cruisers with a degree of vertical armour and first appearing in the cruiser *Leander* of 1880. This in association with the wide belt, previously proposed by William White for both the *Royal Sovereign* and *Centurion* classes, allowed the main strake to be reduced in thickness (the Admiralty Board would not approve any reduction in protective qualities until the coming of Harvey armour which proved to be much more resistant than any compound plates). The Harvey process consisted of taking an all-steel plate and covering with animal charcoal, another plate (to be given a similar treatment) was then placed on top of this to form a sandwich. The plates were then surrounded with bricks, the whole assembly placed in a large furnace and heated for around 2-3 weeks. After this the plates were removed and left to cool for 6 or 7 days. This treatment greatly increased the carbon content of the surface of the plates; a high carbon steel face was thus combined with a standard steel alloy back. The change from one to the other being gradual and without a joint (as in compound armour). Both plates were re-heated in the furnace again and on withdrawal were doused in cold

Victorious at anchor in Beirut in 1900.

Author's collection

water the rapid cooling causing the high carbon steel to become extremely hard thus producing the ideal armour requirement of a super hard face and a soft (resilient) back in one piece. Any forming of the armour plates was done prior to the hardening process.

The deck protection consisted of three thicknesses of plates, two of 1½in and one of 1in, all sloping at an angle of 40° to the ship's side, which was estimated to represent a deflecting resistance equal to about 8in of vertical armour. The wide belt along the waterline provided a constant 9in thickness to a height of 9ft 6in above the waterline compared with only 5in the the *Royal Sovereign*s at a height of 3ft 6in. This protection in *Majestic* was considered sufficient to burst any HE shells, in which case the armoured deck would afford effective splinter protection. Armour piercing shells would have needed to pierce both the 9in side armour and the 4in sloped deck to reach the vitals of the vessel and this was seen as a great improvement over the older methods of armour distribution.

The edges of the flat section of the protective deck were extended right across the ship to the sides by shell plating, the triangular spaces thus formed between the flat and the slope providing watertight flats on each side which could be filled with coal or water; this arrangement was retained in all later battleships with sloping deck protection. As in the *Royal Sovereign* class the protection to the extremities, outside the citadel, were confined to an underwater deck with a cellular layer of watertight compartments above this rising to the middle deck level which was about 3ft 6in above the waterline. These unarmoured ends were a point of criticism owing to the loss of the battleship *Victoria* in June 1893 after being accidentally rammed by the battleship *Camperdown*, the construction of the *Majestic* and *Magnificent* was delayed pending a special investigation into this

TABLE 6: Armour Protection

Main belt:	9in Harvey steel, 220ft long by 15ft wide
Bulkheads:	14in forward, 12in aft
Barbettes:	14in above armoured deck, 7in below
Turrets:	10½in face, 5½in Harvey sides (see gunnery notes)
Casemates:	6in face, 2in side
Protective deck:	3in flat, 4in (40°) slope
Lower deck outside citadel:	2½in forward, 2½in aft, both sloping
Conning tower:	14in face with 8in tube descending to the protective deck. Rear of CT was 12in
Aft conning position:	3in
6in ammunition hoist:	2in

Notes: 4in teak backing to armour. There were 78 watertight compartments outside the armoured citadel and 72 inside. A double bottom was provided from 8ft 9in past the citadel at both ends. Coal bunkers were 11ft and 8ft inboard respectively, behind the armoured belt above the middle deck, and abreast engine and boiler rooms below this.

incident but it was established, after a board of enquiry, that the absence of an armoured belt forward was not responsible for her loss.

MACHINERY

The *Majestic*s were given the same basic machinery as that fitted in the *Royal Sovereign* class, although an extra 1000shp was made available in the former. This gave the same speed but the ships were able to reach their speeds more easily. The new class had improved radius of action, coal stowage being increased to 1900 tons maximum, and 1100 tons at normal load, the latter raised from 900 tons owing to the fact that the board margin was not used up.

It was discovered during the first trials of *Royal Sovereign* in 1892 that the high level of forced draught caused her boilers to leak badly and the steam pressure to fall off so rapidly that she was in danger of complete boiler failure. To avoid this problem the *Majestic* class

The Channel Fleet at anchor, *c*1900. Units of the Flying Squadron (*Royal Sovereign* class) and *Majestic* class.

Author's collection

were not forced to the same extent but nevertheless they achieved the same speed, due mainly to the fact that the new vessels had much finer hull lines. The *Illustrious* and *Magnificent* were fitted with induced instead of forced draught, although the results obtained were slightly less than in the rest of the class. The system was accepted as giving better reliability and safety.

The nominal speed of the *Majestic* class was approximately 1kt faster than in the *Royal Sovereign*s with natural draught and about the same with forced draught although the latter was reached with 1000shp less.

The class had little trouble with their machinery, although there were small problems, one such was the thrust blocks becoming overheated in the *Prince George* whilst running at high power, this was found to be a condenser fault, one of which had perforated. Similar troubles were experienced in *Illustrious* with leaking glands and valves, and some ships suffering from vibration; in general however, other than minor mechanical faults the vessels performed well. In 1903–4 two of the boilers in *Hannibal* and four in *Magnificent, Majestic* and *Mars* were converted to burn oil and coal simultaneously. Each boiler was fitted with 8 sprayers giving a total output of 880lb of oil per boiler per hour at a pressure of 150psi. The radius of action using oil was increased from 6260nm at 10kts to approximately 7000nm, and from 3490nm at 14.6kts to 4420nm at the same speed.

TABLE 7: MACHINERY

Engines:	2 sets of 3 cylinder, vertical, inverted triple expansion engines driving 2 4-bladed improved Griffith propellers.
Cylinders:	40in – 59in – 88in with a stroke of 51in
Boilers:	8 cylindrical single ended, with 4 furnaces each. Water in boilers when full to working height: 120 tons. Heating surface: 24,400sq ft. Revolution of screws: 100–107 (see trials). Working pressure of boilers: 155lb psi.
Weight of machinery as fitted:	*Majestic* 1356 tons, *Mars* 1328 tons, *Jupiter* 1315 tons.
Fuel stowage:	900 tons coal in normal load condition, 1900 tons maximum. The coal stowage was later reduced by 200 tons and 400 to 500 tons oil added in those ships converted in 1903–4.
Radius of action:	With oil sprayers: 7000nm at 10kts. 4420nm at 14.6kts.
Coal consumption:	At full power: 250 tons coal per 24 hours. At ⅝ths power: 140 tons per 24 hours. At economical speed (8kts): 50 tons per 24 hours.
Ships engined by:	*Magnificent* Penn.
	Majestic Vickers.
	Hannibal Harland and Wolff.
	Mars Lairds.
	Jupiter Clydebank.
	Illustrious Penn.
	Prince George Humphreys.
	Caesar Maudsley.
	Victorious Hawthorn Leslie.

The *Majestic*, being the first of the class to complete, was put through a lengthy series of trials. It was during these trials that the Vice-Admiral commanding the Channel Squadron, Lord Kerr, made the following statement whilst watching the vessel perform and having taken many notes with great care:

'I am thoroughly satisfied with the ship, and I think the result is most creditable to the designers and fitters out. We went through manoeuvres and target practice as though we had been in commission for a year already,

Mars c 1904 in all grey paint scheme, with early funnel bands, WT gaff on mainmast and with shields removed from her 3pdr guns. Note the torpedo net shelf at main deck level, she was the only unit of the class so fitted before 1903-04.

Author's collection

but everything went without a hitch. The new ship steers well, and is quicker off the helm than the *Royal Sovereign*'.

APPEARANCE CHANGES

Well proportioned and handsome ships, they were considered by many to be better looking than the *Royal Sovereign*s mainly due to the closer spacing of the funnels and the pronounced shccr at the bows. The masts, each with two large military tops, gave a rather impressive profile, whilst the modified arrangement of the forebridge and conning tower introduced in the first six ships gave them a unique appearance. In this latter arrangement the bridge was built up around the pole foremast, leaving the conning tower clear of obstruction, a departure from previous practice in which the bridge

"MAJESTIC CLASS" BATTLESHIPS.

Armoured layout.

Appearance changes.

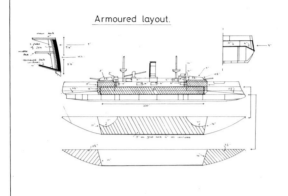

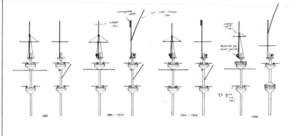

Early rig changes in the "Majestic".

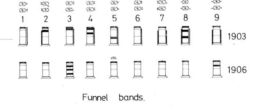

| 1 | 2 | 3 | 4 | 5 | 6 | 7 | 8 | 9 |

1903

1906

Funnel bands.

1910

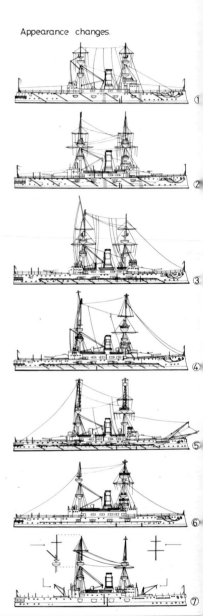

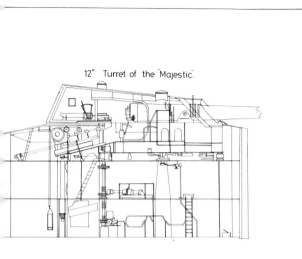

12" Turret of the 'Majestic'.

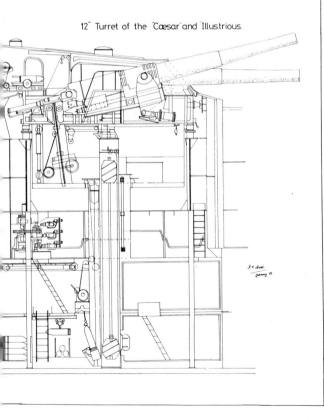

12" Turret of the 'Caesar' and 'Illustrious'.

APPEARANCE CHANGES

1 *Jupiter* 1897 as on trials

2 *Majestic* 1899

3 *Illustrious* 1907

4 *Jupiter* 1910

5 *Prince George* 1915

6 *Magnificent* 1916 as depot ship

7 *Prince George* 1918

FUNNEL BANDS

1 *Majestic*

2 *Mars*

3 *Magnificent*

4 *Hannibal*

5 *Jupiter*

6 *Illustrious*

7 *Caesar*

8 *Prince George*

9 *Victorious*

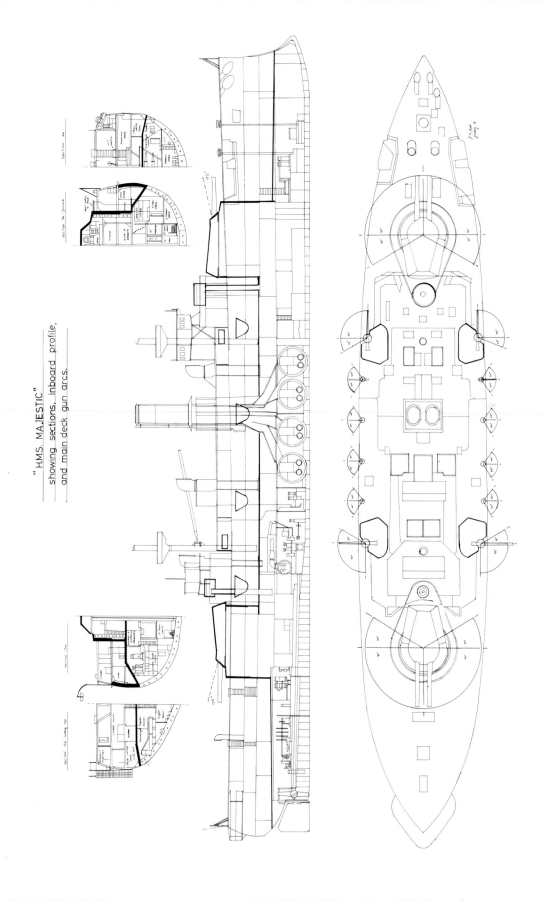

"H.M.S. MAJESTIC"
showing sections, inboard profile,
and main deck gun arcs.

1 *Hannibal*, with early funnel bands (2 black on each), seen entering Portsmouth Harbour in about 1903/4. Although not evident in this photograph she is painted in an experimental light green/brown colour.

Author's collection

2 *Hannibal* leaving Portsmouth about 1910. Note rangefinder drums on the fore and mainmasts, standard funnel bands, no 3pdr in tops, searchlight redistribution and tall WT topgallant mast to main.

Author's collection

3 *Prince George* in 1905-06. Note the searchlight on the lower foremast, the early funnel bands and 3pdr removed from the tops.

NMM, Perkins collection

TABLE 8: STEAM TRIALS OF MAJESTIC 19–20 OCTOBER 1895

Conditions:	Bottom clean, Sea smooth, Wind Force 1.
Propellers:	4 bladed, 17ft ¾in dia with a pitch of 19ft 8⅝in.

30 HOUR TRIAL

Displacement:	13,181 tons.
Revolutions:	85.5 per minute.
IHP:	6075.
Speed:	14.67kts logged.
Coal Consumption:	1.84lb/hp/hour.

8 HOUR TRIAL

Displacement:	13,360 tons.
Revolutions:	100.6
IHP:	10,453.
Speed:	16.9kts.

4 HOUR TRIAL

Displacement:	13,225 tons.
Revolutions:	107.2.
IHP:	12,554.
Speed:	17.8kts.

COLLECTIVE TRIALS of class whilst in Channel Fleet 1904 (8 hour trial).

	IHP	Revs	Speed (kts)
Illustrious	10,073	92.7	15.2
Magnificent	10,365	92.9	15.4
Majestic	9,315	95.9	15.2
Mars	10,025	90.3	15
Hannibal	10,209	95.4	16
Jupiter	10,539	?	16.2
Victorious	10,189	100	16.6
Caesar	10,740	93.7	16.1

As above at ⅗ths power and normal draught,

Illustrious	6,521	84.1	13.6
Magnificent	6,519	80.1	13.1
Majestic	6,765	87.5	14.4
Mars	6,976	84.2	13.97
Hannibal	6,291	84.1	14.03
Jupiter	7,047	?	14.45
Victorious	6,416	88	14.50
Caesar	6,608	83	14.17

was built above the conning tower. The advantages of this arrangement were the increased all-round view from the conning tower and the elimination of the risk of it being obstructed by the collapse of the bridge or parts of it in the event of action damage, and the increased distance between bridge personnel and the blast of the forward 12in gun turret when being fired abeam or abaft that position.

In the last three ships (*Caesar, Hannibal* and *Illustrious*) the earlier system of fitting the bridge over the conning tower was reverted to and this remained a feature of British battleships until the later Dreadnought type *Orion* class in 1909. In William White's January 1893 sketch, the bridge is shown over the conning tower indicating that this had been the original plan for the class.

A flying bridge was fitted in all upon completion, with the exception of the *Magnificent* although she received hers shortly after this. Accommodation was slightly inferior to the *Royal Sovereign* vessels with the cabin arrangements on the whole being more cramped. The bow scroll was abandoned in this class on the grounds of possible interference with the anti-torpedo nets.

As completed the ships are extremely difficult to tell apart, although there were some differences, in particular the following: bridge differences as already noted above.

Jupiter had striking topmasts, a large starfish below the searchlight platforms, an upper yard high on the foremast, tall steampipes abaft the funnels, heavy close fitting funnel caps and small brackets on the inner side of the funnels.

Magnificent had fixed topmasts, charthouse on after flying bridge added in 1896, starfishes, upper yard and funnel caps as in *Jupiter*.

Majestic had light starfish below the searchlight platforms, an upper yard low on the foremast, tall steampipes abaft the funnel and light funnel caps clear of the casing. Topmasts and charthouse as in *Magnificent*.

Mars had topmasts and starfishes as in *Majestic,* two widely spaced steampipes before each funnel and one abaft on the inner side of each funnel (all short), main deck net shelf (only ship so fitted prior to 1903–4).

Prince George had striking topmasts, large starfishes, short steampipes before and abaft each funnel (one only before each funnel) and small light funnel caps clear of casing.

Victorious had topmasts and starfishes as in *Prince George*, steampipes as in *Prince George* except in having two before each funnel and heavy close fitting funnel caps.

Caesar had short steampipes before and abaft the funnels and the upper stay rim on the funnels well below the top.

Hannibal had steampipes abaft the funnels only and to the same height as the funnels and lighter, solid points to the starfish below the searchlight platform.

Illustrious had steampipes abaft the funnels only (but shorter than the funnels) and larger perforated points to the starfish.

Alterations after completion:

1898: Fixed topmasts in *Mars* replaced by striking topmasts stepped forward.

1899: Shields began to be removed from 3pdrs and the number of guns carried in tops were reduced. The guns being relocated on board ship in various positions. Shields removed from all guns by 1902.

1901–2: Wireless Telegraphy fitted with W/T gaff on main topmast.

1902–3: Electric hoists fitted to 6in guns in addition to the hand gear. Experimental oil sprayers fitted in *Hannibal* and *Mars* late in 1902 with the work being completed by February 1903. These two were the first British battleships to be fitted with oil burning gear.

Hannibal, Magnificent and *Majestic* used in experiments with 'Invisible painting' to determine colour to paint ships to replace Victorian colours. *Hannibal* painted greenish brown at first and then black hull and light green upper works. *Magnificent* painted grey and black. *Majestic* black hull and grey upper works. The light green in *Hannibal* proved to be the most difficult to see

*Majestic c*1906 with temporary, red funnel bands.
Author's collection

in some conditions. Final result was an overall grey slightly darker than that which had been used by the German Navy for some time.

1903–4: Net shelf in some ships lowered to main deck level. Fixed topmasts in *Jupiter, Magnificent* and *Majestic* replaced by striking topmasts. Victorian paint replaced by all grey scheme.

1903–4: Funnel bands painted up in some ships. Black top to each funnel with single band below in *Hannibal, Magnificent* and *Majestic*. These bands being used for identification of ships in different squadrons whilst in the Channel Fleet and not for individual ship recognition as with those bands painted up in 1909 (see funnel bands).

Magnificent in late 1908 with an enlarged fore top and a yard fitted to her WT gaff.

NMM – Perkins collection

1905–9: Fire control and rangefinder equipment fitted, the *Magnificent* was given a new oval top fitted in place of the searchlight platform in the foremast. In others original upper fighting top covered in and roofed over being adapted for rangefinder gear although not in *Victorious*. These modifications were all effected from 1905/6 in all except *Majestic* and *Victorious* who were fitted in 1907/8.

In one or two of the first ships fitted, the fire control for the secondary armament was not fitted until as late as 1909. 12pdr guns were removed from the main deck in 1905/6. Some were remounted in various positions, others removed altogether.

Searchlights removed from masts in all ships except *Majestic* (1905/9) but remounted over forward 6in casemates. A great deal of experimental work was carried out in some of the class with regard to the arrangements of the searchlight positions. 2 extra 24in lamps were added in some vessels. Masthead semaphore removed 1906/7. W/T gaff triced up 1907.

1909–14: Small rangefinder mounted in lower foretop in some of the ships (1909–10). Minor changes in the location of 3pdr guns with no more than 4 per ship carried by 1914. Reported in 1912 that 6in and 12pdr were to be replaced in *Magnificent* (then gunnery training ship at Devonport) with 4in quick firing guns although nothing came of this. Nets removed in *Illustrious* and *Magnificent* and more than likely in some of the others from 1912/13. Still in *Hannibal* and *Victorious* by 1913.

W/T gaff replaced by tall W/T topgallant mast in all except *Majestic* (1909/10). *Majestic* still had triced gaff in 1913. Heavy yards removed from mainmast in some. Standard funnel bands painted up in 1909.

1914: Funnel bands painted out.

1915: *Majestic* and *Prince George* modified for service in the Dardanelles Campaign. A small howitzer mounted on roof of each 12in turret to engage shore battery at close range, although found to be of little use in practice and removed by April 1915. Nets fitted and minesweep-

ing gear fitted over the bows. After flying bridge and charthouse removed from *Prince George*. Stockless anchors fitted in this ship. Topgallant fitted to each mast in *Majestic*. Small spotting top at head of fore topmast fitted in both ships and rangefinder baffles fitted around masts but this proved to be of little value and was removed.

Jupiter modified for Suez Canal Patrol in 1915. 12pdr field gun on HA mounting added on fore turret in September 1915 for AA defence. Searchlights reduced to 4. Torpedo nets fitted, after flying bridge removed, and maintopmast reduced to stump.

1915–16: *Hannibal, Magnificent* and *Mars* were disarmed except for 4 upper deck 6in and a few smaller guns, the 12in guns were used to arm the *Earl of Peterborough* class monitors. All three were used as depot ships of some sort.

Magnificent used as troopship September 1915 although it is most likely that *Majestic, Hannibal* and *Mars* were used the same way.

Hannibal reduced to harbour subsidiary service in November 1915 and then the same for *Magnificent* and *Mars* in March 1916.

Victorious disarmed and converted for subsidiary service with the Grand Fleet from September 1915 until February 1916.

Illustrious disarmed and converted as others in November 1915.

1917: *Jupiter* paid off with all 6in and lighter guns removed.

1918: *Prince George* disarmed and converted to depot ship May to September 1918.

Caesar refitted at Malta from September to October 1918 for service as depot ship for the British light forces in the Adriatic.

Main deck 6in removed and small AA gun mounted on after 12in turret, the possibility of a similar fitting forward cannot be ruled out although details are uncertain. Casemate and boat deck searchlights removed, two being remounted on the after flying bridge. Torpedo nets fitted but removed altogether shortly afterwards. Repair shops fitted together with recreation and reading rooms, etc for personnel of the Otranto Barrage patrol craft. Topgallant to mainmast only with full topmast to each mast.

At the end of the war the *Caesar* was the only unit of the class with any armament on board, she retained her four 12in as well as four 6in, all at upper deck level. She had two 36in and four 24in searchlights.

FATES

Majestic Sunk in the Dardanelles 27 May 1915 by *U21*.
Magnificent Scrapped at Inverkeithing from 1921.
Mars Scrapped at Briton Ferry from 1921.
Hannibal Scrapped in Italy from 1921.
Jupiter Scrapped at Blyth from March 1920.
Victorious Scrapped at Dover from 1923.
Prince George Wrecked off Holland and scrapped there (1922).
Caesar Scrapped from July 1922
Illustrious Scrapped at Barrow from 1920.

Jupiter on manoeuvres in 1909, with units of the *Canopus* class following.
Author's collection

TABLE 9: FUNNEL BANDS

As already mentioned the funnel bands in use throughout the period from 1903 to 1904 were for Fleet recognition only and were prone to constant change, they are therefore very unreliable for individual ship indentification. The bands seen in photographs for this period are as follows:

Caesar	None.
Hannibal	Black top with thin black band lower.
Illustrious	None.
Jupiter	One low black band.
Magnificent	Narrow black band on top.
Majestic	None.
Mars	One red band.
Prince George	Two widely spaced black bands.
Victorious	None.

Other markings seen in this period:

Majestic	seen with two red bands.
Magnificent	seen with three dark bands, colour uncertain.
Illustrious	with three dark bands.
Victorious	with a narrow black band.

In 1906 these bands were still being carried but again they are unreliable and changed a great deal:

1906 Bands:

Caesar	None.
Hannibal	None.
Jupiter	None.
Illustrious	None.
Magnificent	Three red bands.
Majestic	None.
Prince George	None.
Victorious	One red band.
Mars	None.

1909–10 saw the introduction of the standard funnel band system which identified individual vessels:

1909–10 funnel bands:

Caesar	None
Majestic	Two red bands.
Magnificent	One red band.
Mars	Three red bands.
Illustrious	Two white bands.
Jupiter	Three white bands.
Prince George	One black band.
Hannibal	One white band.
Victorious	Two black bands.

1 *Jupiter* at anchor in Malta during the Dardanelles campaign, Spring 1915.
Author's collection

2 *Prince George* laid up at Sheerness 1919/20 awaiting scrapping.
Author's collection

3 *Illustrious* partially dismantled at Barrow-in-Furness October 1920.
T W Ward

BOOK REVIEWS

'A CENTURY OF NAVAL CONSTRUCTION – The History of the Royal Corps of Naval Constructors'
by D K Brown RCNC. Published by Conway Maritime Press, March 1983
384pp, 92 photographs, 20 line drawings, glossary, index. ISBN 0 85177 282 X. £20.00

The Royal Corps of Naval Constructors (RCNC) was founded in 1883, and there could be no better tribute to its centenary than this book with its foreword by HRH The Duke of Edinburgh. Nor could there be a better person to write it than D K Brown. Not only is he an Assistant Director of Naval Construction with 30 years' experience in the RCNC (and a deserved mention in the book in his own right for his work on propellers), but, as regular buyers of *Warship* will know, he also has a profound knowledge of the past 150 years of British warship design and a very readable style.

For your money you get a history of the methods, organisation and major personalities of the RCNC, as well as an informed and informative work on the design and development of RN ships from the introduction of iron and steam. Either would be worth the price: together, they represent amazing value. Extensive contributions from senior members of the RCNC past and present have been skilfully worked into the story and add considerably to the reader's understanding.

In order to illustrate the work of modern members of the RCNC, the book starts with a fascinating account of the 'hows and whys' of the design of the postwar *Tribal* class frigates as experienced by a young Constructor, and of *Renown*'s late 1970s refit at Rosyth as seen by the Project Manager. After a full account of the situation in the early and mid-nineteenth century, the main part of the book consists of a chronological account of the work and major personalities of the RCNC. Each chapter deals with the rule of successive Directors of Naval Construction (there is even a section dealing with the inexcusable treatment of Sir William Smith by Winston Churchill) and their successors up to and including the present day and the Type 2400 SSK submarines. The final part consists of individual chapters on the Royal Dockyards, research and development (many fascinating snippets here), education and training, and the wide range of activities undertaken by members of the RCNC, though some of this – particularly the fearsomely difficult training – is also touched on in earlier chapters. It ends with an all too short postscript on the Falklands War.

Although there are clear signs of official reticence in the final chapters, this is not an official history, and it is all the better for that. The author is able to illuminate the book with his personal insights and opinions, for example describing Sir Stanley Goodall as 'probably the most outstanding warship designer of all time', and explaining with admirable clarity why the 1905 battleship *Dreadnought* needed particular care taking over her hull form, and why the cancelled aircraft carrier *CVA-01* would not have been satisfactory had she been built.

D K Brown has a passionate (and justified) pride in the RCNC, and he quite rightly demonstrates how wrong much contemporary and modern criticism of their work has been. In so far as there is a villain in the book it is the Naval Staff, whose demands give rise to some of the most heartfelt (and humorous) quotations from his contributors. This is fair enough, if only because the RCNC has had to suffer much ignorant criticism in the past from naval officers, oversensitive to minor failings in British ships and apparently totally unaware of major flaws in some prominent designs in other navies. However, though D K Brown freely acknowledges mistakes made by the RCNC, I feel that he is overly charitable in his treatment of them. I would also question whether, under the circumstances existing at the time, it was wrong to close the first two schools of naval architecture. The groundwork of naval architecture has not yet been firmly established, and the schools' failings were more significant than their virtues.

These are minor quibbles, though, compared with the sheer volume of excellent work contained within its covers. The book is all the more impressive because so little has been written at this level on either the RCNC itself, its members, or on the designs they produced. As the author says, this book was written about a technical subject by engineers, but it is impossible to write sensibly about ships without any technicalities. There is nothing that a layman cannot understand with the aid of a simple introduction to naval architecture, and the only reason that you need even this is because of the totally inadequate glossary. There is no excuse for this, because the publishers have wasted so much space in the index that there would have been more than enough room to explain everything twice over. Do not let this put you off. If you have any interest in the RCNC, modern warship design, or the Royal Navy, this is a book you must have in your library.

One final point. The frontispiece consists of a photograph of *Dreadnought* on trials in October 1906, signed by the major figures in her design, construction and trials. Some are identified underneath, but some are not. Most of those not identified are in fact from private shipyards, A (Not N) Noble for example being Sir Andrew Noble, then managing director of Armstrong Whitworth. This further illustrates one of the themes of the book, the close relationship between private industry and the Navy in general and the RCNC in particular.

Hugh Lyon

OTHER BOOKS RECEIVED

Red Navy at Sea: Soviet Naval Operations on The High Seas 1956–1980, Cdr Bruce W Watson, USN (Arms & Armour Press/RUSI and Westview Press, October 1982) 245pp, 10 maps, 25 tables, 29 photographs, bibliography, index. An impressive and highly statistical operational survey of the first 25 years of the Gorshkov era.

The Complete Encyclopedia of Battleships and Battlecruisers: A technical directory of all the world's capital ships from 1860 to the present day, Tony Gibbons (Salamander Books, July 1983) 272pp, index, £11.95. Full colour Salamander chronological treatment for

324 classes with line drawings by John Roberts. A full review will be given in *Warship*.

United States Navy Destroyers of World War II John C Reilly Jr. (Blandford Press, May 1983) 160pp, 250 photographs, bibliography, index, £8.95. To be reviewed in *Warship*.

The New Observer's Book of Warships, Hugh W Cowin (Frederick Warne, May 1983) 192pp, index, £1.95. Handy pocket reference in the new large 'Observer' paperback format for 165 of today's classes usefully grouped by general category. Many gaps but at the bargain price a useful primer to avoid going to weightier tomes.

On His Majesty's Service: Observations of the British Home Fleet from the Diary, Reports and Letters of Joseph H Wellings, Assistant US Naval Attaché London 1940–41 edited by John B Hattendorf (US Naval War College Press, Newport RI, 1983) 258pp, 11 photographs, indexes. Free from the publishers (zip code 02841) No 5 in the college's historical monograph series. To be reviewed space permitting.

Soviet Warships: The Soviet Surface Fleet 1960 to the present, John Jordan (Arms & Armour Press, June 1983) 128pp, over 150 illustrations, bibliography, index, £12.95. To be reviewed.

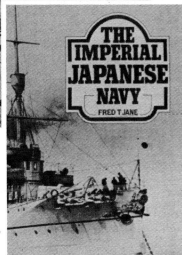

Naval Books

Conway Maritime offer an unrivalled range of authoritative and well-illustrated titles on naval subjects. A free catalogue is available, but some of the leading titles are listed below:

US NAVAL WEAPONS
by Norman Friedman
This exhaustive study by an acknowledged expert on the subject discusses the development and function of every weapon system employed by the US Navy from the birth of the 'New Navy' in 1883 to the present day.
12¼" x 8½", 288 pages, 200 photos, 150 line drawings. ISBN 0 85177 240 4. £18.00 (plus £1.80 p + p)

NAVAL RADAR*
by Norman Friedman
A layman's guide to the theory, functions and performance of seaborne radar systems, from their introduction just before the Second World War to the present day, including a catalogue of every major piece of radar equipment to have seen service with the world's navies.
11" x 8½", 240 pages, 200 photos, 100 line drawings. ISBN 0 85177 238 2. £18.00 (plus £1.80 p + p)

CARRIER AIR POWER
by Norman Friedman
A penetrating analysis of how carrier warfare operates, with extensive data on the ships and their aircraft.
12" x 9", 192 pages, 187 photos, 32 line drawings. ISBN 0 85177 216 1. £12.50 net (plus £2.00 p + p)

ANATOMY OF THE SHIP: THE BATTLECRUISER HOOD*
by John Roberts
The first volume of this new series. Every aspect of the *Hood* is covered in a degree of detail never previously attempted for a recent capital ship, and the standard of line drawings has been highly praised.
9½" x 10" landscape, 128 pages, 24 photos, 320 line drawings. ISBN 0 85177 250 1. £8.50 (plus £1.50 p + p)

ANATOMY OF THE SHIP: THE AIRCRAFT CARRIER INTREPID
by John Roberts
The second in this new series, this volume covers the *Essex* class aircraft carrier which is now being refurbished in New York as a floating Air-Sea-Space museum.
9½" x 10" landscape, 96 pages, 20 photos, 300 line drawings. ISBN 0 85177 251 X. £8.50 (plus £1.50 p + p)

CAMERA AT SEA 1939-1945*
edited by the staff of *Warship*
"A unique collection of some of the best photographs of World War II at sea" – *Sea Power*
12¼" x 8½", 192 pages, 250 photos, 24 colour plates. ISBN 0 85177 124 6. £12.00 (plus £1.50 p + p)

SUBMARINE BOATS
The Beginnings of Underwater Warfare
by Richard Compton-Hall
"Cdr. Compton-Hall has produced a book whose research and many rare photographs and drawings will delight both the technically-minded and the general reader." — *Daily Telegraph*
9½" x 7¼", 192 pages, 173 photos and drawings. ISBN 85177 288 9. £10.50 (plus £1.55 p + p)

CONWAY'S ALL THE WORLD'S FIGHTING SHIPS 1922-1946
The second in this highly acclaimed series, the 1922-1946 volume covers all significant warships built between the Washington Treaty and the end of the wartime construction programmes. With over 1000 illustrations, it is the ultimate reference book on the navies of World War II.
12¼" x 8½", 464 pages, 506 photos, 530 line drawings. ISBN 0 85177 146 7. £30.00 (plus £2.00 p + p)

CONWAY'S ALL THE WORLD'S FIGHTING SHIPS 1860-1905
The first complete listing of all warships between the first ironclad and the *Dreadnought*. " . . . must rank with the all-time great naval reference works . . ." – *The Navy*. " . . . all the thoroughness and attention to detail we have come to expect from Conway Maritime . . . excellent value". – *Ships Monthly*
12¼" x 8½", 448 pages, 471 photos, 506 line drawings. ISBN 0 85177 133 5. £24.00 (plus £2.00 p + p)

A CENTURY OF NAVAL CONSTRUCTION: The History of the Royal Corps of Naval Constructors
by D K Brown R C N C
This behind-the-scenes history of the Royal Navy's designers offers a new insight into the factors governing British warship design from the nineteenth century to the Falklands conflict.
9½" x 6", 384 pages, 92 photos, 20 line drawings. ISBN 0 85177 282 X. £20.00 (plus £1.00 p + p)

DESTROYER WEAPONS OF WORLD WAR 2*
by Peter Hodges and Norman Friedman
A detailed comparison between British and US destroyer weapons, including mountings, directors and electronics. ". . . one of the greatest possible additions to the . . . range of naval books . . ." – *The Navy*
9½" x 7¼", 192 pages, 150 photos, 73 line drawings. ISBN 0 85177 137 8. £7.50 (plus £1.25 p + p)

BATTLESHIP DESIGN AND DEVELOPMENT 1905-1945
by Norman Friedman
The first layman's guide to the design process and the factors governing the development of capital ships. ". . . an eye-opening study of an extremely complex business . . ." – *Nautical Magazine*.
10" x 8", 176 pages, 200 photos, plans and line drawings. ISBN 0 85177 135 1. £8.50 (plus £1.25 p + p)

MODERN WARSHIP DESIGN AND DEVELOPMENT
by Norman Friedman
". . . never before have the problems and parameters of modern warship design been set out so comprehensively, informatively and clearly . . . the book should be read by everyone with a concern for the modern naval scene, professional or amateur, uniformed or civilian." – *Journal of the Royal United Services Institute*
10" x 8", 192 pages, 167 photos, 65 line drawings. ISBN 0 85177 147 5. £9.50 (plus £1.25 p + p)

AIRCRAFT CARRIERS OF THE US NAVY
by Stefan Terzibaschitsch
". . . a definitive history of the US carrier fleet from 1920 until the present day . . ." – *Journal of the Institute of Marine Engineers*
11¾" x 8¼", 320 pages, 322 photos, 94 plans and line drawings. ISBN 0 85177 159 9. £15.00 (plus £1.50 p + p)

*These titles are available in North America from the Naval Institute Press, Annapolis, Md 21402.

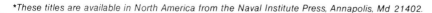

from your Local Bookseller or by post from

Conway Maritime Press Limited
24 Bride Lane, Fleet Street, London EC4Y 8DR

(when ordering direct please add the posting and packing charge noted after the price)

CONWAY
MARITIME PRESS

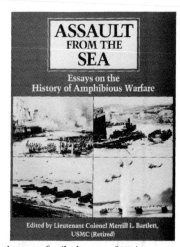